# EVENTFINDER 96

EVENING STANDARD

| | |
|---|---|
| *Publishing Director:* | Don Short. |
| *Editor:* | Brian Cashinella. |
| *Consultants:* | Phoenix PR Services. |
| *Design & Graphics:* | Lynx Art Services Ltd., 172A Selsdon Road, South Croydon, Surrey CR2 6PJ. |
| *Printing :* | Wrightson's Ltd., Hillisgate Rd., Northwood, Isle of Wight. |

*First published October 12, 1995.*

*British Library Cataloguing in Publication Data.*

*© Evening Standard 1995*

*Published in Great Britain for the Evening Standard by Solo Books Ltd., 49-53 Kensington High Street London W8 5ED.*

ISBN No. 1 873939 01 9

# EVENTFINDER '96

Eventfinder '96 is designed
as the ultimate social
guide for the year.

Every Major event is listed
and described. Where ever possible,
contact numbers are given.

Upfront, we have a day-by-day,
month-by-month diary. And all
events are cross referenced in
our supplementary sections
covering a wide spectrum of
interests and activities.

In the centre of Eventfinder '96
you will find a Sportsmaster section
covering all the country's major
sporting events.

And finally we have an index
giving you immediate access
to the entry you require.

So make light of the social year,
dispel those perennial where-to-go
problems. Turn to Eventfinder '96
and we will be back with you in '97
with yet more events to  fill your
essential social life.

● *All events listed are correct at the time of going to press.*
*Unconfirmed events, dates or venues are*
*marked with an asterisk**

Our special thanks are
due to England Soccer
Supremo Terry Venables,
ex - England Cricket Captain
Mike Denness, Britain's
former No1 tennis player
Buster Mottram and the
Evening Standard's star
columnist Peter Mc Kay
for their valued
contributions.

# C O N T E N T S

# Dip in volum

**The Season:** By Peter McKay
*Evening Standard columnist, diarist and
Man About Town*

Some years ago, dipping into The Season, I accompanied Mr. Dai Llewellyn to Royal Ascot in an open-top red Bentley. Mr. Llewellyn, the son of a Welsh baronet, has devoted his life to pleasure. Indeed, he has made a career out of it.

We were attired in morning dress, with top hats, and drank champagne as the chauffeur-driven car - borrowed, I need hardly add - crawled in dense traffic over the last few miles to the course.

At one point we stopped next to three workmen digging a hole in the road. They wore boiler suits

# to this
# e and live!

and orange hard hats and carried shovels. When they caught sight of Mr.Llewellyn and myself they began to laugh.

One of them called out: "What a couple of berks! Is you orf to jolly old Ascot, haw, haw, haw?"

They had a point. We did look ridiculous. Why would any sane person put themselves through this rigmarole?

But Mr. Llewellyn was not to be mocked. Standing up, his hat slightly askew, his wobbling glass tipping champagne down his trousers, he informed the workmen indignantly:

"You think I look ridiculous. That is your point of view. But, if I may say so, you look ridiculous to me."

Happily, the traffic began to move again. To be beaten to death with a workman's shovel while in full morning dress would be a terrible fate. How would friends keep their faces straight at the funeral?

But The Season could not exist without unusual clothes and behaviour. There is so much year-round leisure and so many parties now that The Season's eating, drinking and dressing habits are the only elements which distinguish it from normal life.

Originally, The Season was that time of the year - early to late summer - when the rich, landowing classes took houses in London in order to transact business and to find marriage partners for their offspring.

Now they can get from one end of the country to another by car in a day - as can their offspring - but The Season endures as a social ritual. No-one, other than foreigners who misunderstand it, ever attends all the events in The Season.

The in-bred aristos with implausible chins and noses who congregate at Royal Ascot will not necessarily be seen at Wimbledon. The yotties at Cowes are unlikely to have been at Henley's Royal Regatta.

The Season's association with the aristocracy is now greatly diminished. Literally anyone can join the fun. Even Ascot's Royal Enclosure, where it is possible to fall over the Monarch herself, plays host these days to guests who have enjoyed Her Majesty's hospitality involuntarily elsewhere.

Whatever the occasion - the Derby, International Polo, the Royal Academy Summer Exhibition - the point is to see and be seen, to meet and to be met.

For the elderly, The Season is an opportunity to confirm that the young are ghastly; for the young, it is a time to behave badly.

I remember a post-Ascot party at which young women threw an elderly violinist from the London Symphony Orchestra into a hotel swimming pool. Even the beautiful music and elegance of Glyndebourne does not always discourage down-to-earth behaviour between the sexes. Young women have been ravished in the cars of estate agents at the Garsington opera evenings.

Bad behaviour is always more enjoyable in a formal setting while attired in old fashioned costume.

If you have never dipped into The Season, you have never lived. Study this volume carefully, select the least tiresome-sounding events, tog yourselves and your friends to the nines and jump right in.

Quite soon you will be an expert, deploring the behaviour, clothes, manners and appearance of fellow revellers. And enjoying it thoroughly!

**1**

**Evening Standard 1996 London Parade.**
Tenth anniversary of a spectacular event.
Westminster and West End.
Contact: Lynne Parker 0181 744 0811.

**1**

**Hogmanay.**
First-footing and more than a wee dram to
welcome in '96 at the giant Edinburgh Street
party.  Contact: Barry Wright 0131 557 3990.

**1**

**Llanfarian New Year Sheepdog Trials.**
Get rid of that hangover in the fresh air of the
Welsh countryside.  Aberystwyth, Dyffed.
Contact: J. B. Jones 01970 617590.

**1 - until Jan 6**
**Trafalgar Square Christmas Tree.**
Yes, it even survives the excesses of
New Year's Eve celebrations in the Square.

**1 - until Jan 6**
**CHRISTMAS LIGHTS.**
Free nightly spectacle.
Contact: Oxford Street Association:  0171 629 1234.
Regent Street Association:  0171 491 4429.
Bond Street Association:  0171 629 1682.
Also Covent Garden Christmas Lights.

**1 - until Mar 10**
**In Trust for the Nation.**
Paintings from National Trust houses.
National Gallery, Trafalgar Square.
Contact: 0171 839 3391.  (Opened in November).

**1 - until Feb 18**
**Richard and Maria Cosway.**
Exhibition of works by "Regency Artists of
Taste and Fashion."  Wolfson Gallery,
National Portrait Gallery, St. Martin's Place, WC2.
Contact: 0171 306 0055.

**4 - until Jan 7**
**Autosport International.**
NEC, Birmingham.  Contact: Haymarket
Exhibitions.  0171 402 2555.

**5 - until Jan 14**
**LONDON INTERNATIONAL BOAT SHOW.**
Earls Court Exhibition Centre, London SW5.
World's favourite boat show.
Contact: British Marine Industries and
National Boat Shows Ltd.  01784 473377.

**1 - until Jan 28**
**Royal Academy of Art.**
David Hockney:  A Drawing Retrospective.
Royal Academy of Arts, Piccadilly, London.
(Opened in November.)  Contact: 0171 439 7438.

**1 - until Jan 21**
**Royal Academy of Art.**
Africa:  The Art of a Continent.  Main Galleries,
Royal Academy, Piccadilly. (Opened in October.)
Contact: 0171 439 7438.

**1 - until Jan 5**
**International Model Engineer
and Modelling Exhibition.**
Grand Hall, Olympia, Hammersmith,
London W14.
Contact: Mrs. Christine Basden  01442 66551.

**1 - until Jan 31**
**January Sales.**
Wear Out Your Credit Cards.
See Evening Standard for details.

**1 - until May**
**Leeds International Concert Season.**
Internationally-recognised event.
Town Hall, Leeds, Yorkshire.
Contact: Miss Esther Harrison  0113 247 8336.

**1 - until Jan 14**
**SHAKESPEARE THEATRE SEASON.**
Royal Shakespeare Theatre,
Swan Theatre and The Other Place,
Stratford-upon-Avon, Warwickshire.
Contact:  Royal Shakespeare Theatre 01789-295623
or Information Line 01789 295623.

**3**
**Chelsea Young League Disco.**
Savoy Hotel. In aid of the NSPCC.
Contact: Lesley Edwards  0171 336 7738.

**6 - until Feb 29\***
**British Gas Wildlife Photographer of the Year.**
Natural History Museum, Cromwell Road, South
Kensington. Contact: Gina Dobson 0171 938 9123.

**10 - until Jan 14**
**United Nations 50th Anniversary.**
Central Hall, Westminster.
Commemorative Concert (10); Lecture (13)
and Church Service (14). Contact: 0171 222 8010.

**11 - until Jan 14**
**West London Antiques Fair.**
Kensington Town Hall, W8.
Contact: Penman Antiques Fairs 01444 482514.

**12 - until Jan 26**
**London International Mime Festival.**
South Bank and various other venues,
including Battersea Arts Centre,
Lavender Hill, London SW11.
Contact: Joseph Selig 0171 637 5661.

**14**
**Alexandra Palace Antique & Collectors' Fair.**
Contact: Pig and Whistle
Promotions 0181 883 7061.

**14 - until March 19**
**Edwardian Women Photographers Exhibition.**
Bodelwyddan Castle, nr Rhyl, North Wales.
National Portrait Gallery touring exhibition.
Other venues: Derby Museum and Art Gallery
( April 8 to May 21 ) and Batley Art Gallery,
West Yorkshire ( Sept. 2 - 30 ).

**14**
**Kensington Symphony Orchestra.**
 **Korngold: Die Tote Stadt.**
Royal Festival Hall (Hayward Gallery).
Contact: 0171 921 0800.

**16 - until 25 March**
**LONDON ORIGINAL PRINT FAIR.**
Royal Academy of Arts. Display and
sale of original prints.
Contact: Miss Katherine Jones 0171 439 7438.

**17 - until Jan 21**
**Lapada Antiques and Fine Arts Fair.**
One of the largest events of its kind in Europe.
NEC,, Birmingham. Contact: 0121 780 4141.

**17 - until Jan 21**
**Holiday World.**
King's Hall, Belfast.
Leading international travel exhibition.
Contact: Holiday & Leisure Fairs,
Dublin 00 3531 295 7418.

**17 - until Jan 23**
**Art '96.**
Business Design Centre, 52 Upper Street,
Islington N1. Works of young and established
contemporary artists are sold by specialist dealers.
Contact: 0171 359 3535.

**18 - until Jan 21**
**Knitting, Needlecraft and Design Exhibition.**
Sandown Park Exhibition Centre, Esher, Surrey.
Contact: Robert Ewin: 0117 970 1370.

**19 - until Jan 21**
**BBC Symphony Orchestra.**
Celebrating the work of America
composer Charles Ives. Barbican Centre.
Contact: 0171 638 5403.

**20**
**Rugby Union:**
France v Engand in Paris.
Ireland v Scotland in Dublin.

**20**
**You and Your Wedding Live.**
Everything for the bride to be.
Central Hall, Westminster.
Contact: You & Your Wedding
Magazine 0171 437 0791.

**24 - until Jan 28**
**World of Drawings & Watercolours Fair.**
Park Lane Hotel, Piccadilly, London W1.
Contact: Gay Hutson 0181 742 1611.

**25 - until 12 April***
**Barbican Art Gallery.**
Diaghilev: The Russian Years.
Contact: 0171 638 5403.

**27 - until Jan 28**
**London Bridal Fair.**
Alexandra Palace, N22.
Contact: National Bridal Fairs 01423 707055.

**28***
**Charles I Commemoration.**
The King's Army in 17th Century dress:
St. James's Palace to Banqueting House.
Contact: English Civil War Society 01430 430685.

# February

**30 - until 18 Feb**
**Holiday On Ice.**
Spectacular family variety show. Wembley Arena.
Contact: 0181 900 1234.

**1 - until March 31**
**London Arts Season.**
Contact: Barbara Brett, Town House
Publicity 0171 814 5088.

**1 - until Feb 21**
**Whitechapel Exhibition of Art.**
Works by German painter Emil Nolde
(1867 - 1958). Whitechapel Art Gallery,
Whitechapel High Street, London E1.
Contact: Mark Slader 0171 377 5015.

**1 - until Feb 4**
**Road Racing & Superbike Show.**
Alexandra Palace, N22.
Contact : Shire PR & Marketing 01703 629962.

**2* - until Mar 3.**
**Olympia Fine Art & Antiques Fair.**
Olympia. Contact: 0171 370 8188.

**4 - until March 8**
**International Spring Fair.**
NEC, Birmingham.
Contact: Exhibition Manager 0121 780 4141.

**6**
**Celebration of HM The Queen's**
**Accession to the Throne.**
41-gun salute by the King's Troop at Hyde Park
at Noon and a 62-gun salute by the Hon. Artillery
Company at the Tower of London at 1pm.
Contact: Tower of London 0171 709 0765.

**6 - until March 11**
**Daily Telegraph Period Homes**
**and Gardens Show.**
Olympia. Contact: 01733 394304.

**7 - until March 11**
**Scottish Boat, Caravan, Camping**
**and Leisure Show.**
Scottish Exhibition and
Conference Centre, Glasgow.
Contact: Associated Eventex. 0141 204 0123.

**7 - until March 20**
**Royal College of Art Exhibition.**
A Century of Design. Largest exhibition ever
staged by the College. Contact: 0171 584 5020.

**8 - until April 28**
**Cezanne Exhibition.**
The Tate Gallery, Millbank, SW1.
Part of the London Arts Season.
Contact: LAS 0171 930 9663 or Tate 0171 887 8000.

**8**
**Maple Leaf Charity Ball.**
Grosvenor House, Park Lane.
Contact: 0171 499 6363.

**9 - until March 3**
**Royal Academy of Arts.**
Exhibiton of paintings by Roger de Grey.
Seckler Galleries. Contact: 0171 439 7438.

**10 - until March 17**
**Jorvik Festival.**
Lively event celebrating Viking culture,
including torchlight processions, longboat
races, concerts and firework displays in various
North Yorkshire venues including York.
Contact: Festival Office 01904 611944.

**14 - until April 21**
**At Home with Constable's Cornfield.**
National Gallery, Trafalgar Square, WC2.
Exhibition based around the artist's Cornfield
and its reproductions in prints and other media,
examining public response to the famous image.
Contact: 0171 747 2885.

**14 - until March 17**
**World Cup Cricket.**
India, Pakistan and Sri Lanka.  (See Sport).

**15-until Feb 18**
**Chester Antiques Fair.**
County Grandstand, Chester Racecourse.
Contact: Penman Antiques Fairs 01444 482514.

**15 - until Feb 18**
**International Performance Motor Show.**
Boy racers, racy ladies and enthusiasts' opportunity
to see the latest in motorsport developments.
Olympia, London W14.
Contact: 3D Events 0181 744 1585.

**15 - until Feb 18**
**Destinations '96.**
National travel show giving expert advice and
information on hundreds of holiday locations.
Contact: Consumer Exhibitions 0181 948 1666.

**16 - until April 21**
**Royal Academy of Arts.**
Frederic, Lord Leighton 1830 - 1896.
A Centennial Exhibition (Main Galleries).
Contact: Royal Academy of Arts 0171 439 7438.

**17 - until Feb 19**
**Midland Bridal Fair.**
After January's London fairs for brides Midlands
lasses have their turn.  NEC,, Birmingham.
Contact: National Bridal Fairs 01423 530588.

**17**
**Rugby Union:**
France v Ireland in Paris.
Wales v Scotland in Cardiff.

**17 - until Feb 25**
**National Boat Caravan and Leisure Show.**
A must for outdoor types with wide
selection of boats, mobile homes, camping
and touring equipment.
Contact: BPM Exhibitions: 0121 236 3366.

**18**
**VHF Convention.**
The Radio Society of Great Britain meets.
Sandown Park Convention Centre, Esher, Surrey.
Contact: Peter Kirby 01707 659015.

**21**
**Royal Ulster Agricultural Society Spring Show.**
Northern Ireland's premier
agricultural show at Balmoral, Belfast.
Contact: RUAS 01232 665225.

**22 - until Feb 25**
**International Practical Woodworking Exhibition.**
 Wembley Exhibition Hall.  Europe's
largest show for woodworking enthusiasts.
Contact: Tony Kynaston, Sovereign Exhibition
Management 0181 773 3751.

**23 - until Feb 25**
**Sussex Beer Festival.**
Hove Town Hall, West Sussex.
Dozens of real ales, traditional ciders and perries.
Contact: Keith Freak,Festival
Organiser 01903 261225.

**24 - until Mar 3**
**Bath International Literature Festival.**
Various venues.  Includes readings and
creative workshops.
Contact: Bath Festival Trust 01225 462231.

**24 - until Feb 25**
**International Canoe Exhibition.**
NEC, Birmingham.  Lectures, pool displays and
wide range of canoes and accessories.
Contact: Peter Ingram,
British Canoe Union 01903 795500.

**25**

**Chinese New Year Celebrations.**
Soho, London W1.
Chinese music and entertainment
welcome the Year of the Rat.
Contact: Mr. Malcolm Man
or Mr. K. Wu 0171 734 5161.

**27 - until Mar 3**
**British Philatelic Exhibition.**
Spring Stampex, Royal Horticultural Halls,
Greycoat Street, London SW1.
Collectors from all over the world enter dis-
plays. Contact: Miss Lindsay Towle,
Stampex Ltd. 0171 490 1005.

**27 - until Mar 3**
**The Olympia Fine Art & Antiques Fair.**
Contemporary and traditional works,
including furniture, jewellery,
silver, ceramics, glass.
Contact: P&O Events 0171 370 8188.

**29 - until Mar 3**
**Tenth BT Swimathon.**
Tens of thousands take part
in sponsored swimming events
all over the country. Contact: 0171 406 7335.

**29**
**LEAP YEAR EVENTS.**
Newspaper columns full of ladies
using their traditional right to
ask a partner's hand in marriage!

**\***
**The Great British Innovation & Inventions Fair.**
British inventiveness is legendary.
Will this NEC,, Birmingham show
inspire a new generation?
Contact: Fair Organiser 01202 762252.

## March

**2 - until Mar 3**
**National Dinghy Show.**
Alexandra Palace, N22. THE event of the dinghy
fraternity. More than 70 dinghies fill the two halls.
Contact: Royal Yachting Association 01703 629962.

### Chinese New Year

It is the one year when Leicester Square is
colonised by the Chinese community as the
celebrations of the New Year reach a climax.
From 11.30 am until 5 pm you can see firework displays, martial arts demonstrations,
dancing dragons and Chinese opera.
Then to neighbouring Chinatown in Soho
where the papier-mache monsters startle the
kids and exotic food stalls serve Chinese
specialities al fresco. A warning: wearing
white is considered unlucky. This is the Year
of the Rat, which does not sound too
appetising but in Chinese astrology, the
rodent means prosperity.

**2**
**Rugby Union Five Nations:**
Scotland v England at Murrayfield.
Ireland v Wales in Dublin.

**3**
**The Parrot Show.**
Lots of squawking, talking and preening at this
Parrot Society Event at Sandown Park Conference
Centre. Contact: David Coombes 01234 358922.

**4 - until Mar 16**
**Belfast Music Festival.**
Balmoral, Belfast. Prestigious music, drama and
speech competition which has earned international
fame. Contact: Nancy Mackinnon 01232 611537.

**7 - until Mar 10**
**The BBC Good Food Show 1996.**
Olympia.
One of Britain's major cooking and kitchen events.
Contact: Consumer Exhibitions Ltd. 0181 948 1666.

**7 - until Mar 10**
**The Individual Homes,**
**Home Building & Renovating Show.**
An inspiration for build-it-yourself devotees.
NEC, Birmingham.
Contact: Centaur Exhibitions 0171 287 5000.

**8 - until Mar 10**
**National & Overseas Homebuyer Show.**
Olympia. Largest property sale
of UK and overseas homes.
Contact: Homebuyer Events Ltd., 0181 877 3636.

•
**International Women's Day Show.**
Hackney Empire, Mare Street, London E8.
Contact: Box Office 0181 985 2424.

**9 - until Mar 10**
**RHS Orchid Show.**
Royal Horticultural Society, Old Hall, Westminster.
Contact: Lisa Aitkan 0171 636 7422.

**10**
**Alexandra Palace Antiques & Collectors' Fair.**
Contact: Pig and Whistle
Promotions 0181 883 7061.

**10 - until Mar 11**
**Careers 2000.**
Education, training, careers and jobs
exhibition now in 23rd year. Olympia.
Contact: Jarvis Exhibitions 0181 464 4129.

**11**
**Children's Fashion and Tea Party.**
The Savoy Hotel.
In aid of Cancer Relief Macmillan Fund.
Contact: Charlotte Holmes 0171 887 8249.

**12 - until Mar 14**
**Cheltenham National Hunt Festival.**
Top National hunt meeting attracting punters
by the thousand - especially the Irish!.
Contact: Cheltenham Racecourse 01242 513014.

**14 - until Apr 7***
**DAILY MAIL IDEAL HOME EXHIBITION.**
Earls Court Exhibition Centre. The biggest
consumer home show is now a national institution.
Contact: Earls Court 0171 373 8141
or DMG Angex Ltd. 01895 677677.

**14 - until Mar 17**
**CRUFTS DOG SHOW.**
NEC, Birmingham.
Top dogs compete (and so do their owners!) for
the coveted and world famous Best In Show title.
Contact: The Kennel Club 0171 493 6651.

**14 - until Mar 17**
**National Computer Shopper Show.**
NEC, Birmingham.
Incredible state-of-the-art computer technology.
Contact: Blenheim Events 0181 742 2628.

**14 - until Mar 17**
**Sewing for Pleasure.**
Major attraction for veteran stitchers and
schoolchildren alike. NEC, Birmingham.
Contact: International Craft & Hobby Fair Ltd.
01425 272711.

**14 - until Mar 23**
**Chelsea Antiques Fair.**
Chelsea Old Town Hall, SW3.
A "small and exclusive" fair featuring
43 dealers in arts and antiques.
Contact: Penman Antiques Fairs 014440 482514.

## Daily Mail Ideal Home Exhibition

By far the biggest event of it's kind in the country, this has become a MUST for families from far and wide who flock to London to see the latest in household design, garden design, gadgetry, kitchenware - in fact just about everything for the home and it's environs. Many people spend half their time doing little else but sampling the latest lines in cakes, jams and biscuits. DIY Dads take hours going through the intricaces of new heating methods, double glazing, re-roofing and building a second garage. New brides swoon at the dream kitchens and bedrooms, with their frantic husbands calculating how they are going to afford them. But it is all good fun and eternally popular.

13

**14**
**Mobil Concert Season.**
Leading musicians and orchestras at
Royal Naval College Chapel, Greenwich.
Contact: 0181 305 1818.

**15 - until Mar 17**
**William Walton Festival.**
Queen Elizabeth Hall, Oldham,
Greater Manchester.
In celebration of of Oldham-born musician.
Contact: 0161 911 4072.

**15\***
**Natural History Museum.**
"Meet the Nature Detectives" feature.
Contact: Gina Dobson,
Natural History Museum,
South Kensington 0171 938 9123.

**15**
**Goldilocks Fashion Show.**
The Savoy Hotel, Strand, London WC2.
In aid of the NSPCC.
Contact: Jane Woodfield 0171 336 7738.

**15 - until Mar 18**
**Roaring Twenties Festival.**
Killarney, Co. Kerry, Eire.
Contact: Ms Alex Baradi 00 353 64 41170.

**16 - until Mar 17**
**Record and CD Collectors' Fair.**
Jolson, Sibelius, Presley or Satchmo -
all there at the NEC, Birmingham.
Contact: Exhibitions Manager,
NEC, 0121 780 4141
or P & J Promotions 01273 463017.

**16**
**Rugby:**
The Save & Prosper International:
England v Ireland at Twickenham.
Also Wales v France at Cardiff.

**16 - until Mar 17**
**The London Classic Motor Show.**
Alexandra Palace, N22.
A walk down motoring's Memory Lane.
Contact: Greenwood Exhibitions 01296 631181.

**16 - until Mar 17**
**Miniatura.**
NEC, Birmingham.
(On 15th entry is by pre-booked ticket only.)
Contact: Miniatura 0121 783 2070.

**17 - until Mar 19**
**LONDON INTERNATIONAL BOOKFAIR.**
Olympia, London.
International trade event covering
all aspects of book publishing.
Contact: 0181 948 9828.

**17 - until Mar 19**
**Careers 2000.**
Careers, Training, Education and Jobs event.
NEC, Birmingham.
Contact: Jarvis Exhibitions 0181 464 4129.

**18 - until Mar 22**
**Alternative Fashion Week.**
Old Spitalfields Market, London E1.
Contact: Alternative Arts 0171 375 0441.

**19 - until Mar 21**
**MEMS '96.**
All the latest in electronic music
and recording equipment.
Olympia Exhibition Centre.
Contact: Future Events 01225 442244.

**20 - until Mar 21**
**British Travel Trade Fair '96.**
The big trade get-together.  NEC, Birmingham.
Contact: English Tourist Board 0181 846 9000.

**20**
**Reception & Gala Concert.**
Light opera and classics plus Dinner.
The Guildhall, City of London.
In aid of the National Deaf Children's Society.
Contact: John Trotter 0171 585 1606.

**22 - until June 23**
**David Livingstone and the Victorian**
**Encounter with Africa.**
Wolfson Gallery, National Portrait Gallery,
St. Martin's Place, WC2.  Contact: 0171 306 0055.

**22 - until Mar 30**
**Society of Women Artists Exhibition.**
Central Hall, Westminster.
National and international women artists are
featured in the major annual exhibition.
Contact: Central Hall 0171 222 8010.

**23 - until Mar 31**
**Spring Gardens Week.**
Leeds Castle, Maidstone, Kent.
Contact: 01622 765400.

**23 - until Mar 24**
**London International Dive Show.**
Everything for the sub-aqua
enthusiast or professional.
Contact: The Dive Show Ltd. 0181 977 9878.

**24**
**Chelsea Opera Group.**
Beethoven: Leonora or Bellini: Norma.
Queen Elizabeth Hall, Royal Festival Hall,
London SE1. Contact: 0171 921 0800.

**27**
**Soccer International, Wembley.**
See Sport.

**28 - until June 23**
**Gustave Caillebotte (1848 - 1894):**
**The Unknown Impressionist.**
Seckler Galleries, Royal Academy
of Arts, Piccadilly, London.
Contact: 0171 494 5615.

**29 - until Apr 3**
**London Fashion Week.**
Thirty shows to challenge the world
of high fashion and streetwear.
See Evening Standard for details.

**29 - until Mar 31**
**Bike '96.**
Olympia. Massive collection of bikes
and accessories plus cycling club,
competition and holidays.
Contact: Future Events 01225 442244.

**29**
**Palace of Westminster All Party Ladies'**
**Committee Children's Easter Party.**
Contact: Mrs. William Gunnery 0181 746 8311.

**28 - until Mar 30**
**GRAND NATIONAL MEETING.**
Aintree, Liverpool.
Three-day event culminating in the
Grand National, the world's greatest
steeplechase, on Saturday, March 30,
watched by television viewers worldwide.
Contact: 0151 523 2600.

**31**
**Toy and Train Collectors' Fair.**
Recent years have seen a booming
interest in toys ancient and modern.
NEC, Birmingham.
Contact: D & J Fairs 01526 398198.

*

**Spitalfields Pancake Day Race.**
Politicians, pub teams and office workers
test their skills over 100 yard course against
pancake-hardened veterans.
Contact: Maggie Pinhorn, Alternative Art,
0171 375 0441. (Shrove Tuesday).

*

**The Carnival Ball.**
In aid of SOS. Venue to be announced.
Contact: Jill Davis 0171 637 2500.

*

**Champagne Reception.**
The Guards Museum, SW1.
In aid of the Royal Marsden League of Friends.
Contact: Simon Gold 0171 730 4092.

15

1 - until Apr 8
**Spring Craft Fair.**
Alexandra Palace, N22.
Contact: Marathon Event
Management 0181 665 1082.

\*

**Town Crier Championships.**
Finding the Town Crier of the Year from
the Loyal Company of Town Criers.
Contact: Ted Davy,
Town Crier Beadle 01507 466063.

2\*

**ROYAL CALEDONIAN BALL.**
Grosvenor House.
One of the Season's top social events.
Contact: Mrs. Roger Tym 01264 810363.

4 - until Apr 9
**West Sussex International Youth Music Festival.**
Contact: Concertworld UK 0171 401 9941.

5 - until Apr 12
**Harrogate International Youth Music Festival.**
Choirs, bands, orchestras and dance
groups from many parts of the world.
Various North Yorkshire venues.
Contact Concertworld UK 0171 401 9941.

5 - until Apr 8
**Devizes to Westminster
International Canoe Race.**
Up to 300 canoes set off from Devizes for the
150-mile trip along the Kennet & Avon Canal to the
Thames at Reading and then to Westminster Bridge.
Contact: Competition Secretary 0171 401 8266.

6

**UNIVERSITY BOAT RACE.**
The Oxford versus Cambridge Boat Race
attracts large crowds to the Thames between
Putney Bridge and Mortlake.
Boat Race Ball at The Savoy in the evening.
Contact: Scope Communications 0171 379 3234.

6 - until Apr 9
**York Model Railway Show.**
York Racecourse.
Grown men become enthusiastic schoolboys
amid massive displays of model railway layouts.
Contact: Michael Cook 01653 694319.

\*

**Cable & Satellite.**
The European Broadcasting and
Communication Show (Trade).
National Hall, Olympia.
Contact: Reed Exhibition
Companies 0181 910 7910.

6 - until Apr 11\*
**Fast Food Fair.**
Metropole Exhibition Centre, Brighton.
Leading trade event covering
equipment to franchises.
Contact: Reed Exhibition
Companies 0181 910 7910.

7

**Easter Sunday State Parade and Church Service.**
"Beefeaters" lead dignitaries and invited
guests to service in Tower of London Chapel.
Contact: Tower of London: 0171 709 0765.

7 - until Apr 8\*
**London Harness Horse Easter Parade.**
Battersea Park, SW11.
Contact: 0181 871 7540.

11 - until Apr 14
**Spring Needlecraft Fair.**
Olympia. Displays from museums and
needlecraft school feature along with
everything to do with needlecraft.
Contact: Chris Dawn 01225 442244.

12 - until Apr 14
**National Franchise Exhibition.**
Olympia. Ideal for those wanting to
be their own boss or change their career.
Contact: Blenheim Exhibitions Group
0181 742 2828.

**12 - until Apr 14**
**The Sugarcraft Show.**
Culinary inventiveness and sculpting skills at
Sandown Park Convention Centre, Esher.
Contact: Gerry Fox, Aspen Litharne 01789 720604.

**13 - until Apr 15***
**Environmental Technology.**
NEC, Birmingham. UK's leading trade
show for enviro-equipment and services.
Contact: Reed Exhibition
Companies 0181 910 7910.

**16 - until Apr 21**
**British International Antiques Fair.**
NEC, Birmingham.
Contact: Centre Exhibitions 0121 780 4141.

**19 - until May 4**
**Society of Botanical Artists Exhibition.**
Central Hall, Westminster.
International exhibition with many works for sale.
Contact: Sue Burton 017496 74472.

**19 - until Apr 21**
**International Shooting Sports Association.**
NEC, Birmingham.
Contact: Linc Exhibitions 01733 558900.

**19**
**The Tartan Ball.**
At the Honorourable Artillery Company,
Armoury House, City Road, London EC1.
In aid of Children with Leukemia.
Contact: Suzanne Macrae 0171 404 0808.

**19 - until Apr 21**
**Angling Exhibition.**
NEC, Birmingham.
Contact: Linc Exhibitions 01733 558900.

**19 - until Apr 29***
**Claridge's Antiques Fair.**
Brook Street, Mayfair.
Contact: Bailey's 01278 722341.

**21**
**Official birthday of H.M. The Queen.**
In celebration a 40-gun salute is sounded by
The King's Troop in Hyde Park at Noon and the
Hon. Artillery Company fire a 62-gun salute
from the Tower of London at 1pm.

**21**
**LONDON MARATHON.**
More than 35,000 apply to run the 26 miles of
central London streets but only 25,000 are accepted!
Contact: 0171 620 4117.

### The London Marathon

In 1979, Chris Brasher, inspired by running
the New York Marathon, brought the event to
London. Since then, well over 300,000
runners have completed the 26 mile
385-yard course, raising over £70 million for charity. Starting at 9 a.m.
from Grenwich Park, the route
crosses Tower Bridge, then
tours the recently developed
Isle of Dogs area of East
London before coming
back along the
Embankment to finish in
The Mall. For those who
get thirsty just watching,
there are 92 pubs en route.
But - visitors please note -
being a Sunday they don't open
until noon - by which time the
fastest runners have finished!
However, you'll have plenty of
time to raise a glass to the many
thousands of fun runners who
take six hours or longer to complete the course.

17

**25**
**Mobil Concert Season.**
Summer Music at the Royal Naval College
Chapel, Greenwich.  Contact: 0181 317 8687.

**26 - until Apr 27**
**London Arms Fair.**
Royal National Hotel, nr Russell Square, WC2.
Antique arms, armour, militaria.
Contact: Douglas Fryer,
Arms Fairs Ltd., 01273 475959.

**26 - until Apr 28**
**Harrogate Spring Flower Festival.**
Britain's largest Spring show - and one of the best.
Valley Gardens, Harrogate, North Yorkshire.
Contact: Lisa Aitkan 0171 636 7422 or North of
England Horticultural Society 01423 561049.

*27*
**SILK CUT RUGBY LEAGUE
CHALLENGE CUP FINAL.**
Rugby League's tough professionals provide
one of Wembley's top annual attractions.
Contact: Wembley Stadium 0181 902 8833.

*27*
**Whitbread Gold Cup.**
Sandown Racecourse, Esher, Surrey.
One of the year's top races.
Contact: Racecourse 01372 463072.

**28 - until May 1**
**Food and Drink Expo '96.**
NEC, Birmingham.
Contact: Blenheim Events 0181 742 2828.
❖
**NSPCC BERKELEY DRESS SHOW.**
Berkeley Hotel, SW1
Contact: Joanna Hurthouse 0171 336 7738.
❖
**Blackheath Kite Festival.**
Colourful day as dozens show
off their kite-flying skills.
Contact: Lewisham Council
0181 695 6000 Ext. 6079.

❖
**World Hairdressing Championships.**
Top crimpers go for the title.
Wembley Exhibition Halls.
Contact: 0181 902 8833.

❖ **until July**
**English Civil War campaigns and lifestyle of 1645.**
Battles re-enacted with period dress,
music and entertainment.
Contact: English Civil War Society 01430 430695.

❖
**Art & Sculpture Exhibition.**
National Trust,
Osterley Park House, Middlesex.
Contact: Nat. Trust Thames,
Chiltern Region 01494 528051.

❖
**Rose Ball.**
In aid of The Alexandra Rose Day appeal.
Contact:  Mrs. Gillian Greenwood 0181 748 4824.

❖
**Mirabelle Luncheon.**
Curzon Street, W1.
In aid of the British Red Cross.
Contact: Teresa FitzGerald 0171 201 5059.

❖
**Tartan Ball.**
Honourable Artillery Company, Armour House.
In aid of the Foundation
for Children with Leukemia.
Contact: Miss Suzanne Macrae 0171 404 0808.

❖
**Charity Greyhound Evening at Wimbledon
Stadium.**
In aid of Breast Cancer Campaign.  Contact: Helen
Sandwell 0171 439 1013.

# May

**1 - until May 5**
**London Bird Keeping Festival.**
Alexandra Palace, London N22.
Contact : Sovereign Exhibition
Management 0181 773 3751.

**2 - until May 5**
**BADMINTON INTERNATIONAL HORSE
TRIALS.** Avon. World-class Three- Day Event.
Showjumping, cross-country and dressage.
Contact: Jane Gundry 01454 218272.

**Badminton Horse Trials**

Generally regarded as the biggest and
toughest (Grand National excepted) event in
the equestrian world, the trials attract around
300,000 spectators, two-thirds of them for
cross-country day on Saturday. Eighty com-
petitors are tested over the 30 or so fences -
the course is redesigned every year - covering four and a half miles of the Duke of
Beaufort's estate in the county of Avon.
Dressage on Thursday and Friday, the Big
One on Saturday, then the gentler pursuit of
show jumping on Sunday. Badminton House
is three miles of Junction 18 on the M4. £12
a car (Thursday and Friday), £26 (Saturday)
and £14 (Sunday). Dogs on leads so as not
to scare the horses.

**2**
**Royal Caledonian Ball.**
Grosvenor House , Park Lane.
In aid of Scottish charities.
Contact: Mrs. Roger Tym 01264 810363.

**3 - until May 5**
**Jersey Air Rally.**
Private fliers unite on the Channel Islands.
Contact: Jersey Tourism 01534 500700.

**4 - until May 12**
**Leeds International Music Festival.**
Recitals and concerts of contemporary
music, jazz and Indian music.
Contact: Artistic Director 0113 245 2069.

**4 - until May 6**
**BBC Top Gear Classic and Sportscar Show.**
NEC, Birmingham.
Contact: BBC Haymarket
Exhibitions 0171 402 2555.

**4 - until May 26**
**Brighton International
Festival of Performing Arts.**
Annual event featuring all aspects
of the performing arts.
Contact: Ms Lisa Wolfe 01273 676926.

**4 - until May 6**
**Spalding Flower Parade and Festival.**
Millions of blooms adorn floats for the annual
parade followed by static displays.
Contact: Springfields 01775 724843.
**4**
**Rugby Union:**
Pilkington Cup Final. Twickenham.
Contact: RFU 0181 892 8161.

**6 (or 13)**
**BOC Covent Garden Festival.**
Giving young opera artists chance
to perform to a wider audience.
Contact: 0171 240 0930.

**6**
**Crafts and Countryside Come to Town.**
Morden Hall Park, Morden, Surrey.
Contact: Eloise Harris 01372 453401.

**7 - until May 14**
**British Antique Dealers'
Association Antiques Fair.**
Duke of York's Headquarters, Kings Road, SW3.
Everything from furniture to porcelain.
Also Charity Gala (on 8th).
Contact: Mrs. Gillian Craig, BADA. 0171 589 6108.

**8 - until May 12**
**ROYAL WINDSOR HORSE SHOW.**
Home Park, Windsor Castle. Displays by
Cavalry, RN, Kings Troop and fireworks
display in the Queen's favourite back garden.
Contact: Showground 01753 860633.

**8 - until Sept. 1**
**William Morris Centenery Exhibition.**
Victoria and Albert Museum, South
Kensington. The incredibly diverse world of
Morris's design. From textiles and ceramics to
furniture and stained glass.
Contact: V & A 0171 938 8500.

**8 - until 9 May**
**Spring Into Jazz.**
Barbican Centre, EC2. Two day festival.
Contact: Barbican Centre 0171 638 8891.

**9 - until May 12**
**Festival of Food & Farming.**
Hyde Park, London.
Contact: 01484 428326.

**9**
**Jester Ball at the Grosvenor House.**
In aid of Action on Addiction.
Contact: Rachel Virden 0171 793 1011.

**Jester Ball**

The event was conceived seven years ago as
" a childish ball for grown-ups" with the seri-
ous purpose of raising money for the charity
Action on Addiction. The aperitif is a fair-
ground on the first floor, complete with
coconut shies, jugglers and acrobats. Then
comes dinner and dancing which costs £110
to join in with celebrities and socialites. Last
year the Ball raised £95,000 and Evening
Standard readers were treated to a picture of
Lord Archer sliding down to dinner via a hel-
ter-skelter. A class act to follow.

20

**9 - until May 12**
**Beverley Early Music Festival.**
Medieval architecture and fine music in unique
event at various locations in Beverley, Humberside.
Contact: 01904 658338.

**10 - until May 12**
**Malvern Spring Garden Show.**
Three Counties Showground,
Malvern, Worcestershire.
Contact: 01684 892752.

**11 - until May 26**
**Bournemouth International Festival.**
Up to 80 venues are needed to house events ranging
from opera, rock and jazz to dance and poetry.
Contact: Mrs. T. Weeks 01202 297327.

*
**Aspects of Dance.**
The Wimbledon Theatre.
In aid of The Foundation for
Children With Leukaemia.
Contact: Suzanna Macrae 0171 404 0808.

**11**
**Richmond May Fair.**
Richmond Green, Richmond-on-Thames.
Contact: 0181 948 4464.

**11**
**Soccer.**
FA CHALLENGE Cup Final.
Wembley. (See Sport).

**11 - until May 12**
**Chatsworth Angling Fair.**
Bakewell, Derbyshire. Rods and reels from around
the world at this major international angling event.
Contact: Andrew Cuthbert 01328 830367.

**11 - until May 12**
**Fighter Meet '96**
North Weald Airfield, Epping, Essex.
Europe's leading fighter aircraft show.
Contact: Fighter Meet Ltd. 0181 866 9993.

**11 - until May 12**
**London Dollshouse Festival.**
Kensington Town Hall. Europe's largest.
Contact: Caroline Hamilton 0181 948 1893.

**12**
**Alexandra Palace Antique & Collectors' Fair.**
London N22.
Contact: Pig & Whistle Promotions 0181 665 1082.

**12**
**Covent Garden Mayfayre and Puppet Festival.**
St. Paul's Church Gardens, Bedford Street, WC2.
Celebrating Samuel Pepys' visit in 1662.
Contact: Alternative Arts 0171 375 0441.

**14 - until May 15\***
**Festival of English Wines.**
Leeds Castle, Kent. Jazz backing to tasting of the
fruit of southern English vineyards.
Contact: Leeds Castle 01622 765400.

**14 - until May 18**
**Newbury Spring Festival.**
Berks. Music - from orchestral performances
to jazz - feature in this festival of music and
the visual arts.
Contact: Sheilagh Jackson 01635 32421.

**15 - until Aug 24**
**GLYNDEBOURNE**
**FESTIVAL OPERA SEASON.**
Internationally-known festival presents
a season of top opera productions.
Contact: Festival Office: 01273 812321.

**15 - until May 19**
**Listowel Writer's Week.**
Eire.
Contact: Ms Catherine FitzGerald 00 353 68 21074.

**15 - until May 16**
**British Pig and Poultry Fair.**
Royal Agricultural Society of England
Showground, Stoneleigh, Warwickshire.
Contact: Showground 01203 696969.

**\***
**Living Crafts.**
Hatfield House, Hatfield, Herts.
700 craftsmen and women demonstrate their skills.
Contact: Jean Younger 01582 761235.

**15 - until May 16**
**Countrywide Workshops Fair.**
Mount Ephraim, Faversham, Kent.
Display of ancient crafts and near-forgotten
skills in support of 65 workshops.
Contact: Valerie Wood-Gaiger 01722 326886.

**16**
**Ladies Night at Aintree.**
New event for the racing calender at the Liverpool
racecourse, home of the Grand National.
Contact: Racecourse 0151 523 3600.

**16 - until May 18**
**Devon County Show.**
Exeter. Contact: Festival Office 01392 713875.

**17**
**The Royal Marsden Ball.**
In support of the Royal Marsden Hospital.
Contact: Simon Gold 0181 341 7286.

**17 - until June 2**
**Bath International Festival.**
Avon. Concerts, jazz, opera, exhibitions
and talks at various venues around the Spa town.
Contact: Festival Office 01225 462231.

**17 - until May 19**
**The Cotswold Art Fair.**
Frogmill Inn, Nr Cheltenham, Gloucester.
Contact: Mrs. Caroline Penman 01444 482514.

**17 - until May 23**
**County Wicklow Gardens Festival.**
Eire.
Contact: Brendan O'Connor 00 353 404 66058.

**18**
**Charity Clay Pigeon Shoot.**
In aid of Action on Addiction.
Contact: Rachel Virden 0171 793 1011.

**18**
**Soccer.**
England International.
Wembley Stadium. (See Sport).

**19**

**Ann Boleyn Memorial.**
Each year a basket of red roses is placed on Ann Boleyn's burial site at the Tower of London on the anniversary of her death.

**19**

**World Dock Pudding Championship.**
Mytholmroyd, Hebden Bridge, West Yorkshire. Puddings judged for taste, consistency and presentation.
Contact: Mrs. Sandra Wickham 01422 823630.

**20 - until Sept. 13**
**Minack Theatre Summer Season.**
Porthcurno, Penzance, Cornwall.
Dramatic clifftop open-air theatre sets fabulous backdrop to season of plays and musicals.
Contact: Theatre Management 01736 810181.

**21**

**Ceremony of the Lillies and the Roses.**
Tower of London. In private ceremony, representatives place Eton lillies and Kings College roses on the spot where Henry VI - founder of the two seats of learning - was murdered in 1471.

**21 - until May 24**
**CHELSEA FLOWER SHOW.**
The UK's No. 1 Flower Show. Royal Hospital grounds, SW3. The Queen arrives in horse-drawn carriage on first day. (Monday, Tuesday and Wednesday are RHS Members' days).
Open to public Thursday and Friday .
Contact: 0171 396 4696.
Gala Charity Preview Contact: Mandy Hills, RHS Special Events 0171 630 5999.

**21**

**Gulls Eggs City Luncheon.**
Livery company members and businessmen at Skinners' Hall, EC4, for light charity lunch with the "rare delicacy" of gulls eggs.
Contact: Sally Walton 0171 581 9225.

**22 - until Aug. 26**
**Degas as a Collector.**
Sunley Room, National Gallery,
Trafalgar Square, London WC2.
To coincide with Degas exhibition in the Gallery's Sainsbury Wing, the artist's own collection of paintings, drawings and prints will be displayed.
Contact: National Gallery 0171 839 3321.

**22**
**Brendan Blake Golf Classic.**
In aid of Royal Marsden Hospital. Ealing.
Contact: Simon Gold 0181 341 7286.

**24 - until May 26**
**Richmond Horse Show.**
Old Deer Park, Richmond.
Contact: Richmond Sports Services 0181 941 0485.

**24 - until May 28**
**The 95.8 Capital FM Extravaganza.**
Zany, crazy, nutty fun. Live events and activities galore. Venue to be confirmed.
Contact: Trades Exhibitions 0171 610 3001.

**24 - until May 27**
**Festival of the Sea.**
Bristol. City's historic dockyard fills with 1,000 craft to celebrate Britain's maritime history.
Contact: Festival Office 0117 923 7996.

**24 - until June 1**
**Hay Festival of Literature.**
Hay on Wye, Wales.
Poetry and Literature. Writers, lectures and events.
Contact: Festival Office 01497 821299.

**24 - until June 9**
**Greenwich Festival.**
Contact: 0181 317 8687

**24 - until May 31**
**British Open Ballroom
& Latin American Dance Championships.**
Winter Gardens, Blackpool. Dancers travel from around the world for this annual event.
Contact: 01253 25252.

**25 - until May 26**
**Bedford River Festival.**
The Great Ouse attracts 200 rivercraft,
80 floats and 1,000 performers in one
of the biggest outdoor events of the year.
Contact: Ms Pat Simpson,
Bedford Council 01234 221 622.

**25 - until May 26**
**Air Fete.**
RAF Mildenhall, Bury St. Edmunds, Suffolk.
Military aircraft from NATO countries
and elsewhere converge for one of
Europe's largest air displays.
Contact: Fete Office 01638 823211.

*

**Night of the Stars Ball,**
Grosvenor House, Park Lane.
In aid of Children with Leukaemia.
Contact:  0171 731 8199.

**26 - until June 2**
**International Animation Festival.**
St. David's Hall, Cardiff.
The art of cinema animation.
Contact: British Film Institute 0171 255 1444.

**26 - until May 27**
**Afro Hair & Beauty Exhibition.**
Alexandra Palace, London N22.
Contact: Afro Hair & Beauty Ltd., 0181 883 7061.

**27 - until June 17**
**Isle of Man TT Racing.**
Toughest races on the greatest course in the world.
Contact: 01624 686801.

**27 - until June 7**
**Festival of Dover.**
Pop, classic and jazz - with a maritime
theme for '96 - beneath the White Cliffs.
Contact: Miss S. Pascoe 01304 821199.

**29 - until June 1**
**ROYAL BATH AND**
**WEST OF ENGLAND SHOW.**
Shepton Mallet, Somerset. Royal Patronage for one
of the oldest and largest country shows in the UK.
Contact: 01749 823211.

**29**
**KNELLER HALL OPEN AIR CONCERT.**
Royal Military School of Music Concerts,
Kneller Hall, Twickenham, Middlesex.
Contact: Capt. Ian Peaple 0181 898 8629.

**30 - until June 2**
**Nations Cup Showjumping.**
All-England Jumping Course, Hickstead.
Three Day Event.  Contact: Marathon Event
Management 0181 366 3153.

**30 - until June 2**
**Home PC Show.**
Olympia.  The PC as home office, children's
educational aid, executive ally or the disc-game
addictor!  Fun day for all the family.
Contact: Real Time Events Ltd. 0181 849 6200.

**31 - until Sept 7**
**REGENTS PARK OPEN AIR**
**THEATRE SEASON.**
Inner Circle, NW1.
New Shakespeare Company.
Contact: Sheila Benjamin 0171 935 5756.

*

**Beating the Bounds.**
Tower of London.  Warders and Choristers mark
the boundaries.  In olden days boys were beaten
at points marking the bounday.  Today the
marking points are beaten by the boys.
Provisionally Ascension Day.
Contact:  Tower of London 0171 709 0765.

*

**London Jazz Festival.**
Contact:  0171 437 4797. *

*

**Isle of Wight International Oboe Competition.**
Contact:  Administrator 01983 612451.

*

**International Social Services Spring Fair.**
Kensington Town Hall.  Contact: 0171 735 7184.
*

**International Food Fayre.**
 Olympia.  Contact: 0171 385 1200.

*

**Kensington and Chelsea
Women's Club Spring Fair.**
Commonwealth Institute.
In aid of Marie Curie Cancer Care.
Contact: Jenny McIntyre 0171 201 2368.

*

**Gala Evening.**
Banqueting House, Whitehall, SW1.
Contact: Jane Gaskell,
Animal Health Trust 01638 661111.

*

**Floral Luncheon.**
Savoy Hotel, WC2.
In aid of the Forces Help Society.
Contact: Miss Anne Finley 0171 589 3243.

*

**Royal Marsden Ball.**
Top London venue.
In aid of Royal Marsden Hospital.
Contact: Simon Gold 0171 928 7788

## June

**1\* - until Aug
Barbican Art Gallery - Eve Arnold:
A Retrospective.**
Work by veteran American photojournalist
and Anglophile will be featured to coincide
with publication of her autobiography.
Contact: 0171 638 5403.

**1 - until June 2\*
Balloon and Vintage Car Fiesta.**
Leeds Castle, Maidstone, Kent.
Up to 25 colourful hot air balloons
take to the skies above Leeds Castle.
Contact: 01622 765400.

**1
Louis Vuitton Concourse d'Elegance
Classic Car Competition.**
Hurlingham Club.
Top social event. Invitation Only.

**1 - until June 30
Mick Jagger's National Music Day.**
The idea is to encourage musical talent and
enjoyment. People all over country can take
part by organising an event and registering it.
Contact: National Music Day Events 0171 629 8912.

**1 - until June 2
Open Dance Festival.**
Victoria Embankment Gardens,
Villiers Street, WC2.
Contact: Alternative Arts 0171 375 0441.

**3
Fourth of June - Eton.**
This annual event is always celebrated
on the first Wednesday before June 4.
"The Eton Boating Song" is sung heartily
by boys during day of celebration culminating
in a parade of boats on the Thames.
Contact: Bursar's Office, Eton College,
Windsor, Berkshire 01752 671000.

**3
Coronation Gun Salutes.**
To celebrate the anniversary of the Coronation of
HM The Queen a 41-gun salute will be fired by the
King's Troop in Hyde Park at Noon followed by a
62-gun salute by the Hon. Artillery Company from
the Tower of London at 1pm.

**5 - until June 6
Beating Retreat.**
Floodlit ceremony with trumpeters
and massed bands of the Household Division.
Horse Guards Parade, SW1.
Contact: Box Office 1b Bridge Street, SW1.

**5 - until June 26
Spitalfields Festival.**
Early music and solo recitals in the 18th Century
Wren-pupil church of Christ Church Spitalfields.
Contact: Kate Cockburn 0171 377 0287.

**5 & 7 & 8
Epsom Racecourse: Coronation Cup,
The Oaks, THE DERBY.**
Records of The Derby date back to 1780 making
it the world's oldest recorded sporting event.
Contact: 01372 470047.

## Coronation Day Gun Salute

Those prepared to be deafened by pagentry, get close to the King's Troop of the Royal Horse Artillery at mid-day as they fire a 41-gun salute to celebrate the Queen's Coronation - the traditional 21 plus 20 for a Royal occasion. The Queen retained the term King's Troop as it was her father's wish to retain this ceremonial unit after the Second World War. An hour later, the Honourable Artillery Company loose off another salvo of 62 guns, the additional 20 as the Tower of London is a Royal Residence.

**6 - until Sept. 2**
**Leon Kossoff Exhibition.**
Tate Gallery, Millbank, SW1.
Contact: 0171 887 80006.

**6 - until June 12**
**Appleby Horse Fair.**
Gypsies and travellers arrive in droves for the traditional annual meeting and sale of horses.
Contact: Appleby-in-Westmorland Tourist Centre 01768 351177.

**6 - until June 16**
**The Olympia Fine Art and Antiques Fair.**
Over 400 dealers from all over the world with goodies for the collector, designer and decorator.
Contact: P&O Events 0171 370 8188.

**6 - until June 9**
**Bramham Three-Day Horse Trials.**
Near Wetherby, Yorkshire. Contact: British Horse Society Trials Office 01203 696762.

**6 - until June 10\***
**Cricket:**
Cornhill Test Match. (See Sport).

**6 until June 16**
**Royal College of Art 1996 Degree Show.**
More than 25,000 people from industry, media and public visit the most important event in the College calendar featuring work submitted by students for their finals.
Part One (Fine Art and Textiles) - 6 - 16.
Part Two (Applied Arts, Design) - 26 - July 7.

**6 - until June 20\***
**Hampton Court Palace Music Festival.**
The magnificent royal palace by the Thames. Warm summer evenings and music to match.
Contact: Donna Gelardi 0181 781 9507.

**7 - until June 23**
**49th Aldeburgh Festival.**
Annual arts festival, founded by Benjamin Britten.
Contact: 01728 452935.

**8 - until June 9**
**Move-It Mime Festival.**
Victoria Embankment Gardens, WC2.
Contact: Alternative Arts 0171 375 0441.

**8 - until June 9**
**Woburn Abbey Angling Fair.**
Contact: Andrew Cuthbertson 01328 830367.

**8\***
**The Fleadh.**
Van Morrison and Bob Dylan popped in at previous events. Major open-air Irish music festival at Finsbury Park, London N4.
Contact: The Mean Fiddler Organisation 0181 961 5490.

**8 - until June 30**
**EUROPEAN CUP COMPETITION.**
England are hosts for Europe's top soccer spectacular. Final at Wembley on June 30.
(See Sport).

**8 - until June 9\***
**Biggin Hill International Air Fair.**
Two-day aviation feast of military and
commercial aircraft. Great success in last
year's Helifest may be repeated.
Contact: Air Displays International 01959
572277.

**9 - until Aug. 18**
**228th ROYAL ACADEMY**
**SUMMER EXHIBITION.**
Major annual exhibition of contemporary
art at the Royal Academy of Arts.
Contact: 0171 439 7438.
**Royal Academy Summer**
**Exhibition Private Viewing.**
In aid of Marie Curie Cancer Campaign.
Contact: Jane McIntyre 0171 235 2368.

**9**
**Chelsea Opera Group.**
Puccini: Gianni Schicchi - Il Tabarrao: Suor
Angelica. South Bank (Queen Elizabeth Hall).
Contact: 0171 763 0800.

**10**
**Prince Philip's 75th Birthday.**
Gun Salutes for this event are exactly as
those for the Queen on June 3rd.

**10 - until June 16**
**Stella Artois Grass Court Tennis Championships.**
The Queen's Club.
Contact: Lawn Tennis Association 0171 385 4233.

**11 - until June 13**
**Three Counties Show.**
Malvern, Worcestershire. Agriculture,
horticulture, equestrian and County Set social.
Contact: Showground 01684 892751.

**11 & 12 & 14**
**Sounding Retreat.**
Royal Marines. Horse Guards Parade, SW1.
Massed Bands, pageantry and tradition.
Contact: HQ London District Military
0171 414 2357.

**Biggin Hill International Air Fair**

One of the most magnificent sights anywhere
- hundreds of aircraft of all shapes and sizes,
from old biplanes, "warbirds", helicopters to
state-of-the-art warplanes and passenger
jets. And not just British, either. They come
from all over the world to be seen that this
premier event at Britain's most famous World
War 11 fighter station. Not to be missed by
young and old alike.

**12 - until June 18\***
**BBC Gardeners' World Live.**
NEC, Birmingham
Contact: BBC Haymarket
Exhibitions 0171 402 2555.

**12 (& 26)**
**Royal Military School of Music.**
Kneller Hall, Twickenham, Middlesex.
Fanfares, jazz, dance, military and light music
at open air concerts. (Also in July).
Contact: Capt. Ian Peaple 0181 898 8629.

**13 - until June 22\***
**GROSVENOR HOUSE ART**
**AND ANTIQUES FAIR.**
Items to suit all tastes from £100
to £1 million. Ten day event.
Second night is a charity gala evening.
Contact: Fair Office 0171 495 8743.
**Charity Gala Preview of Grosvenor**
**House Art and Antiques Fair.**
In aid of Tommy's Campaign and SANE.
Contact: Miss Lucy Buxton 0171 620 0188.

**15**
**TROOPING THE COLOUR.**
The Queen's Official Birthday Parade.
Stand tickets by invitation only but plenty
of room to watch the parade of the
Ist Bttn Irish Guards in Horse Guards Parade.
Contact: HQ Household Division 0171 414 2357.

**15 - until June 16**
**Middle Wallop International Air Show '96.**
Army Air Corps attraction for
international entries and visitors.
Contact: International Air Show
Office 01264 384461.

**16**
**Midsummer Poetry Festival.**
Victoria Embankment Gardens, WC2.
Contact: Alternative Arts 0171 375 0441.

**16**
**Children's Open Air Concert.**
National Trust at Polesdon Lacey,
Great Bookham, Surrey.
Contact: Eloise Harris 01372 453401.

**16**
**Singlehanded Transatlantic Yacht Race.**
Starts from Queen Anne's Battery,
Plymouth, Devon, and finishes in Newport,
Rhode Island, USA.
Contact: Royal Western Yacht Club 01752 660077.

**16**
**London to Brighton Bike Ride.**
Motorists become second-class citizens as
27,000 cyclists pedal 52 miles to raise funds
for the British Heart Foundation.
Last year's event raised £1 million.
Contact: British Heart Foundation 0171 935 0185.

**17**
**Ladies Tennis.**
Eastbourne.
Contact: Lawn Tennis Association 0171 385 4233.

**17\***
**The Garter Ceremony.**
The Queen accompanies Knights of the Garter
(Her Majesty's Personal Award) through
Windsor Castle for their annual service.
Contact: Windsor Castle 01753 868286.

**18 until June 21**
**ROYAL ASCOT.**
Ascot Racecourse, Berkshire.
LADIES' DAY - Gold Cup Day - attended by
Queen and other members of the Royal Family.
THE event of the social calendar.
Contact: Grandstand Office 01344 22211.

**20 - until June 23**
**ROYAL HIGHLAND SHOW.**
Newbridge, Edinburgh.
The Scots' national agricultural show.
Contact: Royal Highland Agricultural Society
of Scotland 0131 333 2444.

**21 - until June 23**
**Festival of Speed.**
Against the backdrop of Goodwood House,
near Chichester,Sussex, the Festival has become
the world's biggest event of its kind.
Contact: Festival Office 01243 774107.

**21 - until June 23**
**Gwyl Ilfan Festival.**
The largest Welsh Folk Dancing Festival
at venues around Cardiff.
Contact: Dai Jones 01222 563989.

**24 - until June 28**
**Syon Park Opera.**
The Great Conservatory at Syon House,
Brentford, Middlesex, in aid of The Foundation
for Children with Leukaemia.
Contact: Suzanne Macrae 0171 404 0808.

**24 - until July 7**
**WIMBLEDON
LAWN TENNIS CHAMPIONSHIPS.**
Simply the most prestigious tennis
event in the world.
Contact: All England Club 0181 946 2244.
Ladie's Final - 6th:.
Men's Final - 7th.

**24**
**The Midsummer Ball.**
London Hilton, Park Lane.
This unique black-tie event was created by
Hotel's management to raise funds for charity.
Contact: Sandra Lane 0171 208 4045.

**26 - until July 14**
**City of London Festival.**
St. Paul's Cathedral and the
Tower of London are among the
fabulous historic City buildings
housing the annual arts festival.
Contact: City Arts Trust 0171 377 0540.

**28 - until July 7**
**Glasgow International Jazz Festival.**
Top jazz event with a growing
European reputation.
Contact: Ms Jill Rodger 0141 552 3552.

**28 - until June 29**
**RHS Flower Show.**
Wisley RHS Gardens, Surrey.
Contact: Lisa Aitkan 0171 636 7422.

**28 - until Sept. 22**
**Photographs by Beaton and his contemporaries.**
Exhibition of some of the finest photographs.
Photograph Gallery, National Portrait Gallery,
St. Martin's Place, WC2.
Contact:  National Portrait Gallery 0171 306 0055.

**28 - until June 30✻**
**Glastonbury Festival**
**of Contemporary Performing Arts.**
You don't have to have had hippy
parents to go - but it helps.
Glastonbury took over where Woodstock left off.
Contact Glastonbury Festivals 01749 890470.

**✻**
**Barge Driving Race.**
Annual Thames Lightermen's race.
Teams of one Freeman and two Apprentices steer
cargo barges on the incoming tide from Greenwich.
Contact: Bob Crouch,
The Waterman's Company 0171 283 2372.

**28 - until July 5**
**Shrewsbury International Music Festival.**
Languages from around the world fill the
Shropshire county town as music and
dance groups perform at various venues.
Contact: Concertworld UK. 0171 401 9941.

**29 - until July 7**
**Harwich Festival.**
The East Coast port celebrates with folk dancing,
concerts and exhibitions.
Contact: A. Bartholomew,
Flat 1, High Cross House,
Main Road, Harwich,
Essex CO12 3LP.

**29 - until June 30**
**Cyprus Wine Festival.**
Alexandra Palace, London N22.
Contact: Parikiaki 0171 272 6777.

**29 (& July 6)**
**Leeds Castle Open Air Concerts.**
Leeds Castle, Maidstone, Kent.
Carl Davis conducts the Royal Liverpool
Philharmonic Orchestra.
Climax is the 1812 Overture with guns of
the Royal Artillery and fireworks spectacular.
Contact: Leeds Castle 01622 765400.

**30 - until July 4**
**Royal International Agricultural Society Show.**
One of the world's biggest events
of its kind.  Stoneleigh, Warwickshire.
Contact: Showground 01203 696969.

**30**
**Bromley Pageant of Motoring.**
Norman Park, Bromley.
Contact: John Wexham 0181 658 3531.

**✻**
**Open Air Opera Season.**
Victoria Embankment Gardens, WC2.
Contact: Alternative Arts 0171 375 0441.

**✻**
**Summer Season of Street Theatre.**
Soho Square, W1; Paddington Street Gardens,
W1 and Victoria Embankment Gardens, WC2.
Contact: Alternative Arts 0171 375 0441.

*

**Jazz Plus.**
Victoria Embankment Gardens, London WC2.
Open-air season of contemporary jazz
and multi-cultural music.
Contact: Alternative Arts 0171375 0441.

**30 - July 2**
**Rochester Dickens Festival.**
Celebration of their locally-born author.
Displays, exhibitions and street entertainment
reflecting characters created by Dickens.
Contact: Rochester Tourist
Information Centre 01634 843666.

*

**Broadstairs Dickens Festival.**
Country fair, music, a play and
garden party - at various town venues.
Contact: Festival Organiser 01843 863453.

*

**Timeform Charity Race Day.**
York Racecourse. Contact: 01422 330330.
*

**Chester Racecourse Ball.**
In aid of Cancer Research Campaign.
Contact: Jill Whittingham 010244 348891.

*

**Gentleman and Players Summer Ball.**
Dorchester Hotel, W1. In aid of the NSPCC.
Contact: Jane Woodfield,
London Events 0171 336 7738.

*

**Midsummer Night's Magic Ball.**
Dorchester Hotel, W1. Contact: Caroline Neville
Associates 0181 858 9718.

*

**Magdelene College May Ball.**
Cambridge. In aid of The Prince's Trust.
Contact: Miss Anna Norman 01223 328042.

*

**Midsummer's Ball.**
In aid of Cancer Relief Macmillan Fund.
Contact: Sally Walton
CRMF Events 0171 581 9225.

*

**Blenheim Palace Gala Evening.**
In aid of Cancer Research Campaign.
Contact: Mrs. Trivia Birchley 01923 283770.

*

**Peter Rabbit Children's Party.**
Chelsea. In aid of I Can charity.
Contact: Karen Horn 0171 374 4422.

## July

**3 - until July 7**
**Henley Royal Regatta.**
Five-day international rowing event -
also social and fashion MUST.
Watch the strict dress code, Ladies.
Contact: 01491 572153.

**3 (& 17, 24, 31)**
**Royal Military School of Music.**
Kneller Hall, Twickenham.
More open air concerts.
Contact: Capt. Ian Peaple 0181 898 5533.

**3 - 14**
**Richmond Festival .**
Arts Festival including special Richmond
Theatre programme and Thames-side events.
Contact: Mr. Cutting 0181 332 0534.

**4 - until July 9**
**Cricket.**
Third Cornhill Test -
England v India at Trent Bridge. (See Sport)

**5 - until July 14**
**York Early Music Festival.**
Various venues around York.
Contact: Festival Office 01904 658338.

**6**
**Leeds Castle Open Air Concert.**
Leeds Castle, Maidstone, Kent.
Carl Davis conducts the Royal Liverpool
Philharmonic Orchestra again and another chance
to see and hear their 1812 Overture spectacular.
Contact: Leeds Castle 01622 765400.

**6 - until July 13**
**Cutty Sark Tall Ships Race.**
Leith, Lothian, Scotland. Crews will take part
in two races in '96 - to The Baltic and The Med.
Contact: Peter Smales, The International Sail
Training Association 01590 683900.

**6 - until July 7**
**EURO POWERBOAT CHAMPIONSHIPS.**
Southport, Lancs. The glamour, speed
and thrills of world-class powerboating.
Contact: Jim Cunliffe 01704 533791.

**6 - until July 21**
**Bexley Festival.**
Celebrations include The Bexley Show
at Danson Park, Bexleyheath.
Contact: Ms Bax 0181 303 *7777*.

**9 - until July 14**
**Llangollen International Music Eisteddfod.**
The biggest attraction in Wales attracts
visitors from all over the world.
Contact: Eisteddfod Office 01978 860236.

**9**
**The London to Brighton Classic Car Run.**
For pre-1979 vehicles.
(NOT the Veteran Car Run).
Contact: Greenwood Exhibitions 01296 631181.

**9 - until July 11**
**GREAT YORKSHIRE SHOW.**
Harrogate, Yorkshire. One of Britain's top events
of its kind and a great day out for the whole family.
Contact: 01423 561536.

**9 - until July 14**
**RHS Hampton Court Palace**
**International Flower Show.**
The largest event of its kind in the world,
held amid the historic surrounds of the
Thames-side Palace.
Contact: Sylvia Holder 0171 267 6022.
Charity Gala Evening.
Contact: RHS Special Events 0171 630 5999.

**9 - until July 20**
**Royal Tournament.**
Earls Court, SW5. Pageantry, spectacle -
and fun - as the forces put on some
spectacular displays and competitions.
Contact: Sarah Cater 0171 370 8202.

**10 - 13**
**Buxton Well Dressing Festival and Carnival.**
Ancient ceremony of "dressing"
wells with floral pictures.
Contact: High Peak Borough 01491 411353.

**10 - 13**
**Henley Festival of Music and the Arts.**
Jools Holland and James Galway
are among the attractions.
Contact: Festival Office 01491 411353.

**11 - until July 20**
**Welsh Proms '96.**
Britain's leading orchestras perform.
Contact: St. David's Hall, Cardiff 01222 342611.

**11 - until July 14**
**Phoenix Festival.**
Stratford-Upon-Avon. Rock, jazz, acoustic,
dance - and alternative healing.
Contact: Mean Fiddler Organisation 0181 961 5490.

**11 - until July 14**
**The Natural Health Show.**
National Hall, Olympia. Natural health and
therapy, beauty, health food, exercise and aerobics.
Contact: Global Events 0181 347 6661.

❋
**House of Lords v**
**House of Commons Tug o' War.**
Abingdon Green, Westminster.
No, not more political battles- just a bit of fun.
In aid of Cancer Relief Macmillan Fund.
Other teams include secretaries, clergymen and
soldiers. Dinner in College Gardens follows.
Contact: Jane Cowmeadow 0171 887 8249.

**12 - until Oct. 13**
**BP Portrait Award.**
Wolfson Gallery, National Portrait Gallery,
St. Martin's Place, WC2.
Contact: 0171 305 0055.

**13**
**Yeovilton International Air Display.**
Royal Naval Air Station Yeovilton,
Ilchester, Somerset.
Major international air display and museum.
Contact: RNAS Yeovilton 01935 840551.
✽
**Earth Galleries.**
Natural History Museum. Opening of
spectacular £12million three-storey galleries on
the site of the former Geological Museum featuring
latest in teaching and information techniques.
Contact: Gina Dobson 0171 938 9123.

**13 - until July 14**
**Mid-Wales Festival of Transport.**
Rally of road and agricultural transport and
equipment - some dating from early 1800s - in
parades and displays at Powis Castle, Welshpool.
Contact: Mike Exton 01938 553680.

**13***
**British Grand Prix.**
Formula One motor racing with
World Championship points at stake
for drivers and manufacturers.
Silverstone, Towcester, Northamptonshire.
Contact: 01327 857271.

**13 - until July 14**
**National amateur performing arts competition.**
Marking the 75th anniversary of the
British Federation of Festivals.
Major contests (also on June 20-21)
to find winners at University of Warwick.
Contact: Competition Hotline 0114 230 3557.

**13**
**Cricket:**
Benson and Hedges Cup Final.
(See Sport).

**13**
**Cambridge Big Day Out.**
Crowds of up to 13,000 join the
fun of music and fireworks.
Contact: Cambridge Tourism 01223 358977.

**14**
**Jazz at Claremont Gardens.**
Esher, Surrey.
Picnic and laze to the summer sounds
of jazz in National Trust landscaped gardens.
Contact: Eloise Harris 01372 453401.

**14***
**London Strollathon.**
Last year more than 20,000 pounded
the London streets in aid of charity.
Contact: Elizabeth Dawes 0171 353 6060.

**14 - until July 28**
**Galway Arts Festival.**
Contact: Fergal McGrath 00 353 91 583800.

**15**
**Island of Jersey Floral Festival.**
Contact: 01534 30178.

**16**
**Children's Concert at Polesdon Lacey.**
National Trust event at the Georgian house,
Great Bookham, Surrey.
Contact: Eloise Harris 01372 453401.

**18 - until Aug 4**
**Buxton Opera Festival.**
Spectacular settings in the Spa Town
adjoining the Peak District National Park.
Operatic recitals, cabaret, children's events.
Contact: Festival Office 01298 70395.

**19 - until Sept 14**
**BBC HENRY WOOD**
**PROMENADE CONCERTS.**
Royal Albert Hall, SW7. As much a part of
Summer and England as strawberries and cream.
Contact: Nicola Gould 0171 765 4296.

**21 - until July 23**
**British Music Fair.**
Find a friend with a trade ticket to get you into this strictly 'General Public not admitted' event featuring the latest in keyboards, pianos, printed music, audio and software.
Contact: British Music Fairs 0181 907 8314.

**22 - until July 25**
**Royal Welsh Show.**
Builth Wells, Powys.
Wales's national agricultural show.
Contact: Show Organiser 01749 822200.

**23***
**Highclere Castle Classic Car Show.**
Newbury, Berks. Capability Brown's gardens are the setting for Classic Cars from all over Europe.
Contact: Greenwood Exhibitions 01296 632020.

*****
**Doggett's Coat and Badge Race.**
Started in 1715, the race claims to be the oldest annually-recorded sporting event in the world.
Contact: Bob Crouch,
The Waterman's Company 0171 283 2373.

**BBC Henry Wood Promenade Concerts**

In 1937 the conductor Henry Wood, inspired by a manager called Robert Newman, began "democratising" classical music by presenting cheap concerts for a standing audience - the Promenaders having originated in the 18th century, walking round pleasure gardens listening to music. The vision of the two men has resulted over the last decade in an average of 62 concerts performed over the summer by 32 orchestras under 46 conductors. Prepare to book early and queue for hours for standing room, culminating in the Last Night of the Proms - watch for the Union flags, balloons, Jerusalem and Land of Hope and Glory. Unmissable.

**25 - until July 27**
**Irish National Sheepdog Trials.**
Markethill, Co. Armagh.
One of five major Sheepdog Trials held in Britain and Ireland each year.
Contact: International
Sheepdog Society 01234 352672.

*****
**Stowe Music and Fireworks.**
In aid of the National Trust.
Stowe Landscape Garden, Buckinghamshire.
Contact: Katie Williams 01494 528051.

**26 - until July 28**
**Sussex County Antiques Fair**
**& Mid-Sussex Art Fair.**
Barkham Manor Vineyard, Piltdown, Sussex.
Contact: Penman Antique Fairs 01444 482514.

**27 - until 28**
**Lloyds Bank Harbour Regatta.**
Maritime celebration in Bristol Historic Harbour.
Contact: Bristol Tourism 0117 929 7704.

**30 - until Aug 3**
**Glorious Goodwood.**
Top horse racing in a magnificent backdrop of the Sussex Downs.
Goodwood Racecourse, Chichester, West Sussex.
Contact: Festival Office 01243 774107.

**30 - until Aug 4**
**Millstreet International Horse Show.**
Co. Cork, Eire.
Contact: Thomas Duggan 00 353 29 70039.

**31**
**Sheep '96.**
Major show at Three Counties Showground, Malvern, Worcestershire.
Contact: Show Organiser 01203 696969.

*****
**The Amazing Great Children's Party.**
At the British Genius Site, Battersea Park, London SW8. In aid of The Foundation for Children with Leukaemia.
Contact: Suzanna Macrae 0171 404 0808.

*

**HICKSTEAD.**
The All-England Jumping Course, Hickstead,
West Sussex, is the home to three major
showjumping events.
The Nations Cup (June*),
the Royal International Horse Show (July*)
and the four-day Silk Cut Derby (August*).
Contact: Marathon Event Management
0181 366 3153.

*

**Cartier International Polo.**
Guards Club, Smith's Lawn,
Windsor Great Park, Berks.
Contact: 01784 434212.  (See Equestrian Events).

*

**Golf:**
125th Open Golf Championship..

**26 - 28**
**Cambridge Folk Festival.**
Ethnic music with more popular folk
music in the University city.
Contact: Cambridge Tourism 01223 358977.

*

**Gold Panning Championships.**
Lolancothi Goldmines in Dyfed look like the
Yukon as modern 49-ers pan for gold.
Contact: 01558 650359.

*

**Skean 'Dhu Ball.**
Grosvenor House Hotel.
In aid of Cancer Relief Macmillan Fund.
Contact: Sally Walters 0171 581 9225.

*

**Mayfair Association Summer Party.**
In aid of the Queen Elizabeth
Foundation for the Disabled.
Contact: Mrs. Elizabeth Jordan 01372 842204.

*

**Summer Serenade Concert.**
In aid of Cancer Relief Macmillan Fund.
Contact: Sally Walters 0171 581 9225.

**10 - 13**
**Claremont Fete Chempetre.**
Claremont Gardens, Esher, Surrey.
In aid of National Trust.
Contact: Eloise Harris 01372 453401.

**22**
**Windsor Race Night and Auction.**
In aid of Children with Leukaemia.
Contact: 0171 731 8312.

# August

**1 - until Sept 14**
**BBC HENRY WOOD
PROMENADE CONCERTS.**
 Royal Albert Hall, SW7
 Contact: Nicola Gould 0171 765 4296.

**1 - until Aug 18**
**Royal Academy of Arts Summer Show.**
Burlington House, Piccadilly, London, W1.
Contact: 0171 439 7438.

**1 - until Aug 31**
**Snape Proms.**
Snape Maltings, home of the Aldeburgh Festival,
lets its hair down in this one-month excitement
of rock, jazz, folk, dance and orchestral mayhem.
Snape Maltings, Aldeburgh, Suffolk.
Contact: Proms Office 01728 453543.

*

**Buckingham Palace.**
Opens to the public and attracts thousands
anxious to glimpse the Queen's main residence
(and Sept.).  Dates to be announced.
Contact: 0171 930 4832.

**2 - until 24**
**Edinburgh Military Tattoo and Festival.**
Floodlit ramparts of Edinburgh Castle
are the backdrop to magnificent display
of military pageantry.
Contact: Tattoo Office 0131 225 1188.

**3 - until 10**
**Edinburgh International Jazz Festival.**
Street concerts, late night events and
hundreds of performances.
Contact: Jazz Festival Office 0131 557 1642.

**3 - until 4**
**Sixth annual Classic Car and Country Show.**
Loseley Park, Guildford.
Contact: Mrs. Elizabeth Jordan 01372 842204.

**3 - until 10**
**Cowes Week**
A social season compulsory.
Plus Royal Yacht Squadron Ball,
Cowes Ball and other major social events.
Contact: 01983 295744.

**3 - until 10**
**Royal National Eisteddfod.**
Llandeilo, Dyffed.
Welsh-speaking cultural festival.
Contact: Welsh Tourist Office 01222 499909.

**4**
**Teddy Bears Picnic.**
Battersea Park, SW11.
Contact: Joan Fulton 0181 871 8107.

**\***
**Shrimpers' Regatta.**
Age-old sailing and rowing races in
traditional craft at Gravesend, Kent.
Contact: Bob Crouch,
Waterman's Company 0171 283 2373.

**4**
**Gun Salutes to celebrate HM Queen Elizabeth
The Queen Mother's Birthday.**
King's Troop fires 41-gun salute in Hyde Park
at Noon. The Honourable Artillery
Company's 62-gun salute takes place from
the Tower of London at 1pm.

**6 - until 10\***
**Kerrygold Dublin Horse Show.**
RDS, Dublin.
Contact: Shane Cleary 00 353 1 668 0866.

**6 - until 10**
**Great British Beer Festival.**
Olympia, W14.
Contact: Mr. Cox, CAMRA 01727 867201.

**Battle of Flowers**

More than 3,500 residents of Jersey work
round the year to prepare elaborate floats to
take millions of flowers for the world famous
Floral Carnival and Battle of Flowers. One of
the longest-running festivals of its type, it
was started in 1902 to celebrate the
Coronation of King Edward VII. Flowers used
to be taken from the floats and thrown in a
spirited "battle" between local enthusiasts.
Today, because of the high-tech and elaborate nature of the floats, the battles have
ceased. Instead, hundreds of thousands of
visitors can see the incredible work that goes
into the ornate floats.

**8 - until 9**
**Island of Jersey Battle of Flowers.**
One of Europe's top floral festivals.
Moonlight Parade is on 9th.
Contact: Jersey Battle of Flowers
Association 01534 30178.

**9 - until 11**
**Brecon Jazz Festival.**
Eighty concerts in unique three-day event.
Contact: Festival Office 01874 625557.

**9 - until 11**
**International Balloon Fiesta.**
Awesome sight as up to 150 balloon
or inflatable teams lift into the sky from
Ashton Court Estate, Bristol.
Contact: Bristol Tourist Information 0117 926 0767.

**10 - until 25**
**Edinburgh International Film Festival.**
Lectures, documentaries and cinematic displays.
Contact: Filmhouse 0131 228 4051.

**11 - until 31**
**Edinburgh International Festival.**
World's largest celebration of arts attracting
international figures to official events.
Contact: Festival Office 0131 226 4001.
**Edinburgh FRINGE Festival.**
Now larger than the man event.
Contact: Edinburgh Festival Society,
21 Market Street, Edinburgh EH1 1W
0131 226 5257.

**11 - until Oct. 22**
**Scottish National Portrait Gallery.**
Edinburgh. Richard and Maria Cosway:
Regency Artists of Taste and Fashion exhibition.
Contact: 0131 556 8921.

**12**
**Grouse shooting season begins.**

**13**
**NatWest Cricket.**
Lord's. (See Sport).

**15 - until 18**
**West London Antiques Fair.**
Kensington Town Hall.
Contact: Caroline Penman 01444 482514.

**17**
**World Pipe Band Championships.**
Glasgow. Highland games and sports in
addition to the premier pipe event.
Contact: Royal Scottish Pipe Band
Association 0141 221 5414.

*
**Calor Gas British Open**
**Three-Day Championships.**
Gatcombe Park. World class showjumpers
attempt one of the toughest and most
spectacular courses in jumping.
Contact: 01454 218272.

**20 - ***
**Lombard World Challenge Cricket - Under-15s.**
World cricket stars of tomorrow compete in
knockout tournament that is destined to
become an annual fixture at Lord's,
Trent Bridge and Headingly.

### Edinburgh International Festival

This year is the 50th Festival and the
population of the city will once more double
with half a million culture vultures seeking
drama, music and dance. Last year, the
Festival produced 179 events and was out-
done by "the Fringe" - the Cuckoo in the
nest - with some 2,000. The difference
between the two is that the official Festival
productions are by invitation of the Director -
whereas at the Fringe anything goes and
often does. Book early for tickets ( 0131-
225-5756) - and even earlier for accommoda-
tion or you will be sharing a park bench with
half a clan!

**23 - until 27**
**Beatles Festival.**
Merseyside celebrates the Fab Four.
Contact: Cavern Club, Liverpool 0151 236 9091.

**23 - until 25***
**Reading Festival.**
Largest Alternative Music Festival in the world.
Music on two stages, comedy on third.
Contact: Mean Fiddler Organisation 0181 961 5490.

**24 - until 31**
**Rose of Tralee Festival.**
Co. Kerry, Eire.
Contact: Festival Office 00 353 66 21322.

**25 -until 26**
**NOTTING HILL CARNIVAL.**
Europe's biggest street carnival.
Live stages. Children's Carnival Day is Sunday.
Band spectacular is on Monday.
Contact: Festival Office 0181 964 0544.

**25 - until 26**
**Knebworth '96 Classic Car Show.**
Knebworth Park, Stevenage, Herts.
Up to 1,000 classic cars attract
12,000 visitors annually.
Two hundred autojumble and trade stands.
Contact:  Greenwood Exhibitions 01296 631181.

**29 - until 31**
**Dartmouth Royal Regatta.**
Devon. Top rowing event in addition
to boating and sailing activities.
Contact: Regatta Office 01803 832435.

**29 - until Sept. 1**
**Blair Castle Three-Day Horse Trials.**
Contact: Showground Organisation 01796 481207.

**30 - until Sept. 1**
**Swan Arts Fair.**
Tetsworth, Oxfordshire.
Contact: Caroline Penman 01444 483514.

**30 - until Nov 3**
**Blackpool Illuminations.**
Contact: Tourism Dept. 01253 25212.

**31 - until Sept. 1**
**Chatsworth Country Fair.**
Chatsworth House, near Bakewell, Derbyshire.
Contact: Andrew Cuthbertson 01328 830367.

*
**Teddies '96.**
Ted-lovers' must. Kensington Town Hall, W8.
Contact: Mr. Jackman 01273 697974.

*
**London Riding Horse Parade.**
Rotten Row, Hyde Park.
Contact: Ms Hawley 0181 851 1158.

*
**Cromwell's Day.**
Cromwell Green, Houses of Parliament, SW1.
Contact: Information Desk 0171 219 3000.
*
**International Exhibition of Early Music.**
Royal College of Music, SW7.
Contact: Mr. Askey 01274 393753.

*
**Clarendon Park Autumn Concerts.**
National Trust event.
Contact: Eloise Harris 01372 453401.

*
**Osterley Band Concert with Fireworks.**
Contact: National Trust 01494 528051.
*
**Private View of the Royal Academy's Summer Exhibition.**
Contact: Help the Aged
Special Events 0171 253 2926.

# September

**1 - until Sept 14**
**BBC HENRY WOOD PROMENADE CONCERTS.**
Royal Albert Hall, SW7.
Final fortnight for the Promenaders with
LAST NIGHT OF THE PROMS
(ticket-only) on the 14th.
Contact: Nicola Gould 0171 765 4296.

*
**Buckingham Palace open to the public.**
(Dates to be announced).
Contact: Buckingham Palace 0171 930 4832.

*
**Queen Charlotte's Birthday Ball.**
Grosvenor House, Park Lane.  Major event in the
traditional Season.  (Date to be confirmed)
Contact: Birthday Ball Office 0181 741 4653.

**1 - until 7**
**Regents Park Open Air Theatre Season.**
New Shakespeare Company productions.
Contact: Sheila Benjamin 0171 935 5756.

**1\* - until Dec**
**Erwin Blumenfeld (1897 - 1969).**
Barbican Art Gallery. Exhibition of one of
the leading figures in the history of photography.
Contact: Barbican 0171 638 5403.

**1 - until Nov 3**
**Blackpool Illuminations.**
Five miles of lighting attract visitors from all over
the world to the north-west's showpiece resort.
Contact: Tourism Dept. 01253 25212.

**1 - until Nov\***
**Shakespeare Theatre Season.**
Swan Theatre and The Other Place,
Stratford-upon-Avon plus touring company.
Contact: Royal Shakespeare
Theatre Company 01789 295623.

**1 - until 4**
**International Jewellery Exhibition (Trade).**
Earls Court. Showpiece event featuring latest
in merchandise plus tools and machinery.
Contact: Earls Court
Olympia Marketing 0171 370 8011.

**\***
**Alexandra Palace Antique & Collectors' Fair.**
London N22.
Contact: Pig & Whistle Promotions 0181 883 7061.

**2 - until 8\***
**Farnborough Aerospace**
**Exhibition and Air Show.**
World famous aviation event.
Contact: Air Show Office 0171 938 3666.

**3 - until 21**
**Leeds International Concert Season.**
International performers and major works.
Contact: Principle Music Office 0113 247 6336.

**4**
**MUCK South West '96.**
Major agricultural show at the Royal Bath and
West Showground, Shepton Mallet.
Contact: Show Organiser 01749 822200.

**5 - until 8**
**Burghley Horse Trials.**
Top three-day showjumping event
at Burghley, Stamford, Lincolnshire.
Contact: Show Office 01780 52131.

**5 - until Sept. 8**
**Sea Shanty Festival.**
Hull, Humberside.
Contact: Linda Martin 01482 595726.

**7**
**Royal Highland Gathering. Braemar.**
Meeting of The Clans and The Royals
from nearby Balmoral in Deeside.
Contact: Gathering Organisation 01339 755377.

**7**
**Cricket.**
NatWest Bank Trophy Final at Lord's.
(See Sport).

**\***
**European Women of Achievement Luncheon.**
Grosvenor House Hotel, W1.
Contact: Tricia Birchley 01923 283770.

**9 - until 14**
**International Eisteddfod.**
Llangollen, North Wales, attracts the world to its
annual international gathering featuring music,
dance, poetry and Welsh culture.
Contact: Welsh Tourist Office 01222 499909.

**10 - until 11**
**City of London Flower Show.**
Guildhall, EC2. Flowers amid the
skyscrapers in the City's annual event.
Contact: Mr. Jones 0181 472 3584.

**10**
**Chinatown Mid Autumn Festival.**
Lion-dancing, Chinese Theatre, singing
and variety on stage at Gerard Street,
Chinatown.
Contact: Malcolm Man or K. Wu
0171 734 5161.

*

**Horsemen's Sunday.**
St. John's Church, Hyde Park Crescent, W2.
Contact: Ross Nye 0171 262 3791.

*

**Park Lane Hotel Antiques Fair.**
Piccadilly, W1.
Contact: Bailey Fairs 01277 366663.

**17**
**Battle of Britain Open Day.**
Biggin Hill Airport, Kent. Displays by historic
and wartime aircraft including the Spitfire.
Contact: Air Displays International 01959 572277.

**18 - until 19**
**Dairy Farming.**
Town and Country event at the National
Agriculture Centre, Stoneleigh, Warwickshire.
Contact: 01926 887477.

*

**London Thames Festival.**
Riverside activities celebrating Old Father Thames.
Contact: London Thames Festival 0171 700 6453.

*

**Tweseldown Novice Horse Trials.**
Tweseldown Racecourse, Hampshire.

**12 - until 21**
**Chelsea Antiques.**
Chelsea Old Town Hall, SW3.
Contact: Penman Antique Fairs  014440 48251.

**13 -until 15**
**Great Autumn Flower Show.**
Harrogate, Yorkshire. Major event
on the gardening calendar.
Contact: Lisa Aitkan, NHS, 0171 636 7422.

*

**The Great River Race.**
Viking Boats, Chinese dragonboats, Hawaiian war
canoes in races from Richmond to Isle of Dogs.
Contact: Stuart Wolff 0181 398 9057.

**14**
**Last Night of The Proms.**
Henry Wood Promenade Concerts,
Royal Albert Hall, Kensington Gore, London SW7.
0171 589 8212.

**15 - until 23**
**Southampton International Boat Show.**
Mayflower Park, Southampton. Largest
show of its kind in Europe.
Contact: British Marine
International Federation 01784 473377.

## Battle of Britain Open Day

Reinstated by popular demand last year after
a break of 15 years and including a thrilling
but spine-chilling re-enactment of an attack
on Biggin Hill by the Luftwaffe during the
Battle of Britain, this show is a must for all
aircraft buffs and Second World War Memory
Laners. There are now about 25 Spitfires flying in Britain, lovingly  restored by enthusiasts, along with similar Hurricanes,
Messerschmitts and numerous other contemporary aircraft. Also screaming overhead
will be classic jets like the Meteor, Vampire
and the Gnat trainer. An investment in
earplugs sounds wise.

**15 - until 27**
**Chelsea Craft Fair.**
Chelsea Old Town Hall, Kings Road.
Contact:  Craft Council 0171 278 7700.

**15**
**The Spitalfields Show.**
Annual Horticultural Show in the
Old Spitalfields Market, London E1.
Contact: Alternative Arts 0171 375 0441.

\*

**Wellington Ball.**
Cavalry & Guards Club, 127 Piccadilly.
Major social and charity event.
Contact: Catherine O'Kelly, Cancer Research
Macmillan Fund 0171 581 9225.

**16 - until 22**
**North Wales Music Festival.**
St. Asaph, Clwyd.  Choirs, soloists and
music in the splendour of rugged North Wales.
Contact: Welsh Tourist Office 01222 499909.

**17 - until 18**
**RHS Great Autumn Show.**
Royal Horticultural Society's major
seasonal event at RHS Halls, Westminster.
Contact:  RHS 0171 636 7422.

**19 - until 22**
**BLENHEIM INTERNATIONAL
HORSE TRIALS.**
Spectacular three-day event at Blenheim Palace,
Woodstock, Oxfordshire.
Contact: Trials Office 01993 8133335.

**19 - until Dec 15**
**The Twentieth Century: The Age of Modern Art.**
Major exhibition at Royal Academy of
Arts, Piccadilly, London.
Contact: RA 0171 494 5615.

**21**
**Egremont Crab Fair.**
Gurning, greasy-pole races in traditional
street festival in Egremont, Cumbria.
Contact: Mr. W. Rickerby 01946 820376.

**25 - until Jan. 5, '97**
**Peter Blake:**
**Associate Artist at the National Gallery.**
Exhibition showing the work produced by Blake
during his two years in the National Gallery.
Sunley Room, National Gallery, Trafalgar Square,
London WC2.  Contact: 0171 839 3321.

\*

**Consumer Electronics Show.**
Earls Court, SW5. Latest electronics wizardry.
Contact:  Blenheim Exhibitions 0181 742 2828.

**26 - until Nov 5**
**Soho Jazz Festival.**
Top bands and soloists perform
in various venues in Soho.
Contact:  Festival Office 0171 437 6437.

**26 - until 29**
**Galway Oyster Festival.**
Contact: Ms Ann Flanagan 00 353 91 22066.

**26 - until 29**
**The National Woodworker Show.**
Sandown Park Conference Centre, Esher, Surrey.
Contact: John Lenton,
Nexus Special Interests 01442 66551.

**27 - until 28**
**London Arms Fair.**
Royal National Hotel, Russell Square, WC2.
Antique arms, armour and militaria.
Contact:  Douglas Fryer,
Arms Fairs Ltd., 01273 3475959.

\*

**The National Self-Build Homes Show.**
Alexandra Palace, London N22.
Contact: 0191 690 8888.

\*

**London Docklands Seafood Fair.**
Isle of Dogs.
Contact: 0171 512 4414.

\*

**Osberton Horse Trials.**
Worksop, Nottingham.

\*

**Duxford Air Show.**
Duxford Airfield, Cambridge.
Contact: Airfield 01223 835000.

\*

**The Ladies' Autumn Luncheon.**
The Queen's Stand, Epsom Racecourse.  In aid of
the Queen Elizabeth Foundation for the Disabled.
Contact:  Mrs. Elizabeth Jordan 01372 842204.

❋

**Late Summer Dance.**
Hurlingham Club.
In aid of Royal Marsden Junior League of
Friends.
Contact: Simon Gold 0171 928 7788.

❋

**British Art Fair.**
Royal College of Art, SW7.
Contact: Gaynor  Hutson 0181 742 1611.

# October

1  **Pheasant shooting begins.**

**1 - until Nov 3**
**Blackpool Illuminations.**

**1 - until Dec. 15**
**The 20th Century: The Age of Modern Art.**
Major exhibition. Royal Academy of Arts.
Contact: 0171 439 7438.

**2 - until 6**
**HORSE OF THE YEAR SHOW.**
Wembley Arena, Empire Way, Wembley.
Annual showjumping extravaganza.
Contact: British Showjumping
Association 01203 693088.

**3 - until 6**
**20th International Kinsale Gourmet Festival.**
Co. Cork, Eire.
Contact: Peter Barry 00 353 21 774026.

**4 - until 6**
**Nottingham Goose Fair.**
Forest Recreation Ground, Nottingham.
Traditional English Fair, arguably the oldest.
Contact: David Poole 0115 941 7324.

**5 - until 6**
**Eastside Bookfair.**
Old Spitalfields Market, London E1.
Contact: Alternative Arts 0171 375 0441.

**7 - until 19**
**Irish Life Dublin Theatre Festival.**
Contact: Tony O'Dalaigh 00 353 1 677 8122.

❋

**Thames Barrier**
- full tidal closure, Eastmoor Street, Woolwich SE7.
Contact: 0171 474 6951.

❋

**International Festival of Fine Wine and Food.**
Olympia 2, W14.
Contact: Gary Thompson 0171 782 6874.

**13**
**Shakespeare in Spitalfields.**
Old Spitalfields Market, London E1.
Contact: Alternative Arts 0171 375 0441.

**14 - until 18**
**Tattersalls Newmarket Yearling Sales.**
Park Paddocks, Newmarket. Top owners,
buyers, agents and racing folk bid for some
of the best-bred bloodstock in the world.
Contact: Tattersalls Ltd. 01638 665931.

**14**❋
**Disney On Ice Spectacular.**
Three-weeks at Wembley Arena.
Contact: 0181 902 8833.

**16 - until 18**
**Armoury House Art Fair.**
Hon. Royal Artillery Headquarters,
City Road, London EC1.
Contact: Caroline Penman 01444 482514.

❋

**Trafalgar Day Parade.**
Trafalgar Square, SW1. Sea Cadets commemorate
anniversary of Nelson's victory at the Battle
of Trafalgar on October 21, 1805.
Contact: National Heritage 0171 211 6200.

**17 - until Jan. 19, '97**
**Making & Meaning:  Rubens's Landscapes.**
The National Gallery holds the most outstanding
group of the artist's landscapes in the world.
Exhibition examines technique and motivation.
Contact: National Gallery, Trafalgar Square,
London WC2 0171 839 3321.

**18 - until 27**
**Autumn Ideal Home Exhibition.**
Home-makers and improvers can see the latest in consumer products at the National Exhibition Centre, Birmingham.
Contact: Exhibitions Manager 0121 780 4141.

**19 - until Jan. 6**
**The Grand Tour Exhibition.**
Tate Gallery, Millbank, SW1.
Contact: 0171 887 8000.
*
**London Fashion Week.**

**19 - until 26**
**British International Motor Show.**
NEC, Birmingham. UK's top motoring event.
(Press on 15th, Trade 16-18).
Contact: Show Office 0171 235 7000.

*
**Wexford Opera Festival. Eire.**
Contact: Jerome Hynes 00 353 53 221447.

**22 - until 27**
**Autumn Stampex.**
Royal Horticultural Society Halls, SW1.
Contact: Joanna Peck 0171 332 0534.

**25 - until 28**
**Cork Jazz Festival.**
Contact: Ms Emily Twomey 00 353 21 270463.

**25 - until Nov 2**
**Guildford Book Festival.**
Authors, poets, literary talks and lunches. Children's events.
Contact: Arts Administrator 01483 259167.

**26 - until Nov. 3**
**DAILY MAIL INTERNATIONAL SKI SHOW.**
Olympia. The UK's top ski event.
Contact: ANGEX 01895 677677.

**26**
**Fantasy In The Sky Fireworks Spectacular.**
Flambards Village Theme Park, Helston, Cornwall.
Contact: David Edwards 01326 573404.

*
**Knitting & Stitching Show.**
Alexandra Palace, N22.
Contact: Gordon Thomas 0181 690 8888.

**31 - until Nov 3**
**Kensington Antiques Fair.**
Kensington Town Hall.
Contact: Caroline Penman 01444 482514.

*
**The World's Biggest Coffee Morning.**
The British Heart Foundation hopes to beat its own Guinness world record by encouraging people all over the country to go for coffee between 8am - 12-noon at pre-arranged locales. Proceeds to the British Heart Foundation. Date and details to be released later.
Contact: BHF 0171 987 2088.

*
**The Daily Telegraph**
**Cheltenham Festival of Literature.**
Contact: Festival Office 01242 521621.

*
**Pearly King and Queens Harvest Festival Service.**
St Martin in the Fields, WC2.
Annual Pearly Kings and Queens get-together.
Contact: St. Martin's 0171 930 1862.

*
**Wildlife Photographer of the Year.**
British Gas-sponsored competition verdict.
Natural History Museum, SW7.
Contact: Gina Dobson 0171 938 9123.

*
**Punch and Judy Festival.**
Covent Garden, WC2.
Contact: Prof. Percy Press 0181 802 4656.

*
**Dance Umbrella.**
Dance, from ballet to bop, at different venues in the capital.
Contact: Dance Umbrella 0181 741 4040.

❋
**Billy Smart's Circus.**
Old Deer Park, Richmond.
Contact: Richmond Arts Section 0181 331 0534.

❋
**Blue Cross Celebrities and
their Pets Exhibition and Auction.**
Savoy Hotel.  In aid of Blue Cross Animal
Charity.  Contact: Tania Mitchell 01993 822651.

❋
**Champagne Reception.**
Christie's, King Street, SW1.
In aid of Iris Fund for the Prevention of
Blindness.
Contact: Mrs. V. Wride 0171 928 7919.

❋
**Hennell Commitment to the Arts.**
Reception and Exhibition of jewellery
and silver at Spencer House, SW1.
Contact: Mrs. Ann Norman-Butler
0171 629 6888.

❋
**Sotheby's Charity Auction and Dinner.**
In aid of Cancer Relief Macmillan Fund.
Contact:  Sally Walton 0171 581 9225.

❋
**Wine Dinner.**
Top hotel venue.  In aid of Tommy's
Campaign and the MacIntyre Trust.
Contact: Ms Helen Otton 0171 620 0188.

## November

❋
**STATE OPENING OF PARLIAMENT**
(Date to be announced).

**1 - until 3**
**DAILY MAIL INTERNATIONAL SKI SHOW.**
Olympia. (See October).

**1 - until 3**
**Blackpool Illuminations.**
The Promenade, Blackpool, Lancs.
(See October).

**London-Brighton Veteran Car Rally**

Centenery year of the event originally called
the "Emancipation Run" to celebrate the rule
that a man with a red flag had to walk in
front of the horseless carriage.  The speed
limit consequently shot up to 12 mph.
Expect around 450 cars - all at least 90 years
old and worth an estimated £20 million - to
putter away from The Serpentine between 7-
30 a.m. and 9 a.m., drivers heavily wrapped
up and goggled, heading over Westminster
Bridge and down the A23.  The run is not a
race.  There is a speed limit of 20 m.p.h. And
beware the term "old crock" which is a red
rag to a proud owner with a handy starting handle.

**1 - until Jan. 6**
**The Grand Tour Exhibition.**
Tate Gallery, Millbank, SW1.
Contact: 0171 887 8000.

**1 - until Dec. 15**
**The 20th Century: The Age of Modern Art.**
Exhibition at Royal Academy of Arts, Piccadilly.
Contact: 0171 439 7438.

**1 - until 3**
**Kensington Antiques Fair.**
Kensington Town Hall, W8.
Contact: Caroline Penman 01444 482514.

**1 - until January**❋
**Hockney Portraits exhibition.**
Wolfson Gallery, National Portrait Gallery,
St. Martin's Place, WC2.
Contact: 0171 306 0055.

**2**
**Grand Firework Spectacular.**
Breathtaking display of fireworks at
floodlit Leeds Castle.
Contact: Leeds Castle, Maidstone,
Kent 01622 765400.
Plus Guy Fawkes Night celebrations
throughout UK.

**3**
**100th RAC London to Brighton**
**Veteran Car Run.**
Probably the oldest continuous motoring event
in the world. From Hyde Park to Brighton.
Contact Colin Wilson 01753 681736.

**3 - until 4\***
**British Equine Event.**
Royal Agricultural Society specialist event
at the National Agricultural Centre,
Stoneleigh Park, Warwickshire.
Contact: Show Organiser 01203 696969.

**5**
**25th Grand Firework Display.**
Crystal Palace Park.
Contact: Ian Middleton 0181 699 1363.

**8 - until 23**
**Royal Miniature Society's**
**101st annual exhibition.**
Central Hall, Westminster.
Fascinating miniatures from paintings to
sculpture.
Contact: Sue Barton 017496 74472.

**8 - until 9\***
**The Dolls House Fair.**
Alexandra Palace, London N22.
Contact: Gordon Thomas 0181 690 8888.

**8 - until 9\***
**The Teddy Bear Fair.**
Alexandra Palace, London N22.
Contact: Gordon Thomas 0181 690 8888.

**\***

**Olympia Fine Art and Antiques Fair.**
Olympia, W14.
Contact: Victoria Borwick 0171 370 8211.

**13\***
**The Lord Mayor's Procession and Show.**
Marching bands and floats parade to celebrate
the inauguration of a the new Lord Mayor
of London. Fireworks at dusk.
Contact: Pageantmaster 0171 606 3030.

**9 - until 27**
**Belfast Festival at Queens.**
Contact: 01232 667687.

**\***

**Christmas Lights.**
Celebrities switch on festive lights.
Contact Oxford Street Association 0171 629 1234.
Regent Street Association 0171 491 4419.
or Bond Street Association 0171 629 1682.
Also at Covent Garden.

**10 or 13\***
**Remembrance Day Service and Parade.**
Cenotaph, SW1.

### Remembrance Day Parade

At two minutes to 11, a parade of some
10,000 ex-servicemen and women, including
the diminishing number of World War One
veterans, will be called to attention around
the Cenotaph. The Queen, other members
of the Royal Family and leading political figures, take their positions. Big Ben, striking
11 signals a two-minute silence when those
who have died in the service of their country
will be remembered. Then comes the haunt-
ing sounds of Last Post, followed by the traditional laying of Poppy wreaths, led by Her
Majesty.

43

**11 - until 12**
**Duchess of Kent opens Christmas Market.**
In aid of Cancer Relief MacMillan Fund at
Royal Horticultural Society Hall, Westminster.
Contact: Charlotte Holmes 0171 887 8249.

**20 - until Dec. 1**
**Huddersfield Contemporary Music Festival.**
Renowned event featuring music,
dance, film and theatre.
Contact: Festival Office 01484 425082.

**24 - until 27**
**Royal Smithfield Show and Agricultural
Machinery Exhibition.**
Earls Court.
Contact: 0171 370 8011.

**25\***
**House of Lord v**
**Commons Speedo Charity Swim.**
Hurlingham Club. In aid of Women's Caring Trust.
Contact: 0171 730 8883.

**29 - until Dec. 1\***
**Christmas Craft Fair.**
Alexandra Palace, London N22.
Contact: Gordon Thomas 0181 690 8888.

**29 - until Dec 1**
**National Cage Bird & Aviary Show.**
NEC, Birmingham.
Contact: Tony Kynaston,
Sovereign Exhibition Management 0181 773 3751.
\*
**Job Scene London.**
Alexandra Palace, London N22.
Contact: Gordon Thomas 0181 690 8888.

\*
**London Film Festival.**
National Film Theatre, South Bank,
SE1 and other venues.
Contact: Press Office 0171 928 3535.

\*
**London Grand Christmas Parade.**
(See Evening Standard for details).

\*
**World Travel Market.**
Earls Court. The global travel industry forum.
Contact: Earls Court Olympia 0171 370 8011.
\*
**Healing Arts.**
Royal Horticultural Society Halls, SW1.
Contact: Mrs. Spar 0171 938 3788.

\*
**Good Woodworking Show.**
Alexandra Palace, N22.
Contact: Future Publishing 01225 442244.

\*
**NSPCC Goldilocks Fashion Show.**
Savoy Hotel.
Contact: Jane Woodfield 0171 335 7738.

\*
**Help the Aged Gold Awards Luncheon .**
Top London venue.
Contact Help the Aged
Special Events 0171 253 2926.

\*
**City of London Sinfonia.**
Barbican charity concert in aid of Help the Aged.
Contact: Help the Aged
Special Events 0171 253 2926.

\*
**Breast Cancer Campaign Ball.**
Top London venue.
Contact: Helen Sandwell 0171 430 1013.

\*
**Barnardo Ball.**
Celebrity event at top venue
in aid of Barnado's charity.
Contact: Mrs. William Pull 0171 602 7833.

\*
**Royal Star and Garter Winter Ball.**
In support of Disabled Sailors, Soldiers and Airmen.
Contact: David Burland 0181 948 8865.

\*
**The Fall Ball.**
Grosvenor House Hotel, W1.
In aid of Age Concern.
Contact: Miss Lucy Colyer-Jordan 0181 679 8000.

# December

**1 - until Jan. 6**
**The Grand Tour Exhibition.**
Tate Gallery, Millbank, SW1.
Contact: 0171 887 8000.

**1 - until Dec. 15**
**The 20th Century: The Age of Modern Art.**
Exhibition at Royal Academy of Arts, Piccadilly.
Contact: 0171 439 7438.

**1\***
**The Creative Ball.**
Grosvenor House, Park Lane.
Contact: 0171 499 6363.

**1 - until Jan 6**
**Christmas Lights.**
London's West End and Covent Garden
get lit-up for Christmas.

**5 or 12 - until Jan 6**
**Christmas Tree.**
Trafalgar Square, SW1.
City of Oslo's goodwill Norwegian spruce tree.
Carols are sung around the tree nightly.
Contact: Mrs. Philo 0171 211 6393.

**5**
**Carol Concert.**
Royal Naval College Chapel, Greenwich.
Contact: Organiser 0181 317 868767.

**6 - until 7**
**Winmau World Darts Championships.**
Venue to be confirmed.
Contact: British Darts Organisation 0181 883 5544.

\*
**Guards Chapel Carol Concert.**
Wellington Barracks. (invitation only).
In aid of British Heart Foundation.

**11**
**Royal guest at Christmas Carol Concert.**
Guards Museum, Wellington Barracks. Martyn
Lewis introduces celebrity at event. Reception follows. In aid of Cancer Relief Macmillan Fund.
Contact: Catherine O'Kelly 0171 581 9225.

\*
**Great Christmas Pudding Race.**
Covent Garden Piazza, WC2.
Contact: Cancer Research Campaign 0181 446 4226.

**18 - until 22**
**International Showjumping Championships.**
Olympia, W14.
Contact: Ms V Bull 0171 370 8206.

**25**
**Peter Pan Cup Swimming Race.**
Serpentine, Hyde Park, W2.
Contact: Mr. Titmus 01753 544441.

**26**
**King George VI Chase.**
Kempton Park, Sunbury on Thames, Middlesex.
Popular Boxing Day meeting.
Contact: Kempton Park Racecourse 01932 782292.

\*
**Varsity Rugby.**
Annual Oxford v Cambridge
rugby match at Twickenham.
Contact: Rugby Football Union 0181 892 8161.

\*
**The Festive Table & Christmas Craft Fair.**
Alexandra Palace, N22.
Contact: Mike Nugent 0181 366 3153.

\*
**Boxing Day.**
Packs of foxhounds gather in towns many parts of
the country for the traditional Boxing Day Meets.

**30 - until Jan 1**
**Edinburgh Hogmanay.**
First footing and a wee dram or two
in Scotland's street festival to welcome in 1997.
Contact: Unique Events 0131 557 3990.

**31**

**Allendale Baal Festival.**
Costumed local people parade with burning barrels of tar on their heads to celebrate the New Year. Market Square, Allendale, Northumberland.

**31**

**New Year's Eve Celebrations.**
Trafalgar Square.

*

**NSPCC Cinderella Ball.**
Savoy Hotel hosts top social/charity event.
Contact: Jane Woodfield,
London Events 0171 335 7738.

*

**Lifeboat & Mermaid Ball.**
Top venue for party in aid of Royal National Lifeboat Institution.
Contact: Mrs. Sue Clifton 0171 834 5264.

*

**Guildhall Carol Concert.**
In aid of the Royal British Legion.
Contact: Julia Maude 0171 973 0637.

*

**Feathers Ball.**
Teenage event in aid of Feathers Club.
Contact: 0181 748 8660.

## The Evening Standard EVENTFINDER.'97.

Do you have an event you would like to be considered for placing - FREE - in next year's **Eventfinder?**
If so. please fill in this coupon and post it to the address below to reach us as soon as possible but no later than June 30th, 1996.

Name of Event

_____

_____

_____

Date(s) on which it (they) will take place

_____

_____

_____

Location(s)

_____

_____

_____

Brief description of event(s)

_____

_____

_____

_____

Name, Address, Telephone and Fax number of organiser/s (for publication)

_____

_____

_____

_____

Please send your coupon (with publicity/ photographic material, if available) to:

The Events Editor, Eventfinder '97,
Solo Books Ltd., 49-53 Kensington High Street, London W8 5ED.

## Useful Dates for 1996

| | |
|---|---|
| New Year's Day (Bank Holiday UK and Eire) | Jan. 1 |
| Bank Holiday (Scotland) | Jan. 2 |
| Martin Luther King Day (Hol. US) | Jan. 15 |
| Australia Day (Hol. Australia) | Jan. 26 |
| Ramadan (First day - approx) | Jan. 22 |
| St. Valentine's Day | Feb. 14 |
| George Washington's Birthday (Hol. US) | Feb. 19 |
| Ash Wednesday | Feb. 21 |
| St. David's Day (Wales) | Mar. 1 |
| Commonwealth Day | Mar. 11 |
| St. Patrick's Day (N. Ireland & Eire) | Mar. 17 |
| Mother's Day (UK) | Mar. 17 |
| British Summer Time starts | Mar. 31 |
| Passover (First Day) | Apr. 4 |
| Good Friday (UK & Eire) | Apr. 5 |
| Easter Day | Apr. 7 |
| Easter Monday (England, Wales & Eire) | Apr. 8 |
| HM Queen Birthday | Apr. 21 |
| St. George's Day (England) | Apr. 23 |
| May Day (England & Wales) | May 6 |
| Spring Bank Holiday (Scotland) | May 6 |
| Islamic New Year (1417) | May 19 |
| Victoria Day (Canada) | May 20 |
| Spring Bank Holiday (England & Wales) | May 27 |
| May Day (Scotland) | May 27 |
| Memorial Day (USA) | May 27 |
| Father's Day (UK) | June 16 |
| Canada Day (Canada) | July 1 |
| Independence Day (USA) | July 4 |
| Holiday (N. Ireland) | July 12 |
| Holiday (Scotland & Eire) | Aug. 5 |
| Late Summer Bank Holiday (England & Wales) | Aug. 26 |
| Labor Day (US & Canada) | Sept. 2 |
| Jewish New Year (5757) | Sept.14 |
| Yom Kippur | Sept.23 |
| Holiday (US & Canada) | Oct. 14 |
| British Summer Time ends | Oct. 27 |
| Remembrance Sunday (UK) | Nov.10 |
| Veterans' Day Holiday (US) | Nov 11 |
| Thanksgiving Day (US) | Nov 28 |
| St. Andrew's Day (Scotland) | Nov 30 |
| Christmas Day | Dec.25 |
| Christmas Holiday (UK & Eire) | Dec.26 |

## Useful addresses

**National Gallery,**
Trafalgar Square, London WC1 5DN.
Tel: 0171 389 1785.  Fax: 0171 839 3526.

**Tate Gallery,**
Millbank, London SW1P 4RG.
Tel: 0171 887 8000.

**Royal Academy of Arts,**
Burlington House, Piccadilly, London W1V 0DS.
Tel: 0171 494 5615.  Fax: 0171 439 4998.

**National Portrait Gallery,**
St. Martins Lane, Trafalgar Square,
London WC2H 0HE.
Tel: 0171 306 0055.

**Barbican Art Gallery,**
Barbican Centre, London EC2Y 8DS.
Tel: 0171 638 5403.

**Natural History Museum,**
Cromwell Road, London SW7.
Tel: 0171 938 9388.

## AGRICULTURE, ANIMALS & PETS

### CRUFTS DOG SHOW.
Who's the Top Dog? More than 100 breeds compete for the coveted and world famous Best In Show title at the NEC, Birmingham. Contact: The Kennel Club 0171 493 6651. (March 14 -17)

### The Parrot Show.
Proud owners from all over the country travel to Sandown Park Conference Centre, Esher, Surrey, for this Parrot Society event. Contact: David Coombes 01234 358922. (March 3)

### London Bird Keeping Festival.
Bird lovers flock to Alexandra Palace, London N22, for this chirping celebration of bird breeding. Contact: Sovereign Exhibition Management 0181 773 3751. (May 1 - 5)

### British Pig and Poultry Fair.
Royal Agricultural Society of England Showground, Stoneleigh, Warwickshire. Contact: Showground 01203 696969. (May 15 - 16)

### ROYAL BATH AND WEST OF ENGLAND SHOW.
Shepton Mallet, Somerset. Royal Patronage for one of the oldest and largest country shows in the UK. Contact: Show Office 01749 823211. (May 29 - June 1)

### Royal International Agricultural Society Show.
Stoneleigh, Warwickshire. The major event of the Agricultural/Social calender attracting visitors from all over the world to see the latest in British agriculture. Contact: Showground 01203 696969. (June 30 - July 4)

### ROYAL HIGHLAND SHOW.
Newbridge, Edinburgh. The Scots' national agricultural show. Contact: Royal Highland Agricultural Society of Scotland 0131 333 2444. (June 20 - 23)

### Sheep '96.
Shepherds, breeders and food experts' annual get-together at Three Counties Showground, Malvern, Worcestershire. Contact: Show Organiser 01203 696969. (July 31)

### Royal Welsh Show.
Builth Wells, Powys. Livestock, horticulture, forestry and farm machinery at the national agriculture event. Contact: Royal Welsh Agricultural Society 01982 553683. (July 22 - 25)

### MUCK South West '96.
Major agricultural show at the Royal Bath and West Showground, Shepton Mallet. Contact: Show Organiser 01749 822200. (Sept. 4)

### Dairy Farming.
Town and Country event at the National Agriculture Centre, Stoneleigh, Warwickshire. Contact: Show Office 01203 696969. (Sept. 18 - 19)

### Blue Cross Celebrities and their Pets.
Exhibition and Auction attended by the famous at the Savoy Hotel, Strand, London WC2 in aid of Blue Cross Animal Charity. Contact: Tania Michell 01993 822651. (Oct.*)

**Royal Smithfield Show and Agricultural Machinery Exhibition.**
The country comes to Earls Court, London, for this showcase event attracting the world's food and farming experts. Contact: Earls Court Exhibition Centre 0171 370 8011.  (Nov. 24 - 27*)

**National Cage Bird and Aviary Show.**
NEC, Birmingham.
Contact: Tony Kynaston, Sovereign Exhibition Management 0181 773 3751.  (Nov. 29 - Dec 1)

## ANTIQUES

**GROSVENOR HOUSE ART AND ANTIQUES FAIR.**
The celebrated fair where items range from a hundred pounds to a million. The second night of the ten-day event is a charity gala evening.  Contact: Fair Office, Grosvenor House 0171 495 8743.   (June 13 - 22*)
*Charity Gala Fair Preview in support of Tommy's Campaign and SANE.*
*Contact: Miss Lucy Buxton 0171 620 0188.*

**West London Antiques Fair.**
Kensington Town Hall, W8.
Nearly 100 dealers display antiques to 1870 on three floors of the Town Hall in this twice-yearly event. Contact: Caroline Penman 01444 482514.  (Jan. 11 - 14 & Aug. 15 - 18)

**Alexandra Palace Antique & Collectors' Fair.**
Contact: Pig and Whistle Promotions 0181 883 7061.  (Jan. 14)

**Lapada Antiques and Fine Arts Fair.**
One of the largest events of its kind in Europe. Dealers sell wide range of antiques. The Forum, NEC, Birmingham.
Contact: 0121 780 4141.  (Jan. 17 - 21)

**The Olympia Fine Art and Antiques Fair.**
Olympia, W14.
A United Nations of top dealers (US, Australia, all-Europe and UK  - 400 of them) present works for the collector, designer and decorator.
Contact: P&O Events 0171 370 8188.
(Feb. 27 - March 3, June 6 - 16 & Nov.*)

**Chester Antiques Fair.**
County Grandstand, Chester Racecourse.
Contact: Penman Antiques Fairs 01444 482514.
(Feb. 15 -18)

**Chelsea Antiques Fair.**
Chelsea Old Town Hall, SW3. The "small and exclusive" fair featuring 43 dealers of antiques and art for sale.  Contact: Penman Antiques Fairs 014440 482514.  (March 14 - 23 & Sept. 12 - 21)

**British International Antiques Fair.**
NEC, Birmingham.
Giant gathering of antiques dealers and experts.
Contact: Centre Exhibitions 0121 780 4141.
(Apr. 16  - 21)

**Claridge's Antiques Fair.**
Brook Street, Mayfair.  Up-market venue for up-market range of antiques.
Contact: Bailey's 01278 722341. (Apr. 19 - 29*)

**London Arms Fair.**
Royal National Hotel, Russell Square, WC2.
Antique arms, armour, militaria.
Contact: Douglas Fryer,
Arms Fairs Ltd. 01273 475959.
(Apr. 26 - 28 & Sept. 27 - 28)

**British Antique Dealers' Association Antiques Fair.**
Duke of York's Headquarters, Kings Road, SW3.  Features everything from furniture to porcelain.  Also Charity Gala on 8th.
Contact: Mrs. Gillian Craig,
BADA 0171 589 6108.  (May 7 - 14)

**London Dollshouse Festival.**
Kensington Town Hall,  Hornton Street, W8.
Europe's largest event of its genre.
Contact: Caroline Hamilton 0181 948 1893.
(May 11 - 12)

**Alexandra Palace Antique & Collectors' Fair.**
London N22. Popular show attracting
bargain-hunters galore.
Contact: Pig & Whistle
Promotions 0181 665 1082. (May 12)

**Sussex County Antiques Fair
& Mid-Sussex Art Fair.**
Barkham Manor Vineyard, Piltdown, Sussex.
Beautiful country setting for this first
joint antiques-art fair at Barkham.
Contact: Penman Antique Fairs 014440 482514.
(July 26 - 28)

**Kensington Antiques Fair.**
Kensington Town Hall.
Contact: Penman Antiques 014440 482514.
(Oct. 31 - Nov. 3)

## ARTS & LITERATURE

**228th ROYAL ACADEMY
SUMMER EXHIBITION.**
Royal Academy of Art, Piccadilly, SW1.
Major annual exhibition of contemporary art.
Contact: RA 0171 439 7438.
**Royal Academy Summer Exhibition.**
Private Viewing in aid of Marie Curie
Cancer Campaign.
Contact: Jane McIntyre 0171 235 2368.
(June 9 - Aug. 18)

**David Hockney.**
A Drawing Retrospective in Seckler Galleries,
Royal Academy of Arts, Piccadilly. Began in
November. Contact: Press Office 0171 439 7438.
(Jan. 1 - 28)

**Africa: The Art of a Continent.**
Main Galleries, Royal Academy of Arts,
Piccadilly. Began October.
Contact: Press Office 0171 439 7438.
(Jan. 1 - 21)

**In Trust for the Nation.**
Paintings from National Trust houses.
Exhibition at the National Gallery,
Trafalgar Square. Began in November.
Contact: 0171 227 4820. (Jan. 1- Mar. 10)

**Richard and Maria Cosway:
Regency Artists of Taste and Fashion.**
Exhibition of their work at the Wolfson Gallery,
National Portrait Gallery, St. Martin's Place, WC2.
Contact: NPG 0171 306 0055. (Jan. 1 - Feb. 18)

**Art '96.**
Business Design Centre, 52 Upper Street,
Islington N1. Works of young and
established contemporary artists are sold
by 80 specialist dealers.
Contact: BDC 0171 359 3535. (Jan 17 - 23)

**World of Drawings
& Watercolours Fair.**
Park Lane Hotel, Piccadilly, London W1.
Fifty leading galleries and dealers offer
original works for sale.
Contact: Gay Hutson 0181 742 1611.
(Jan 24 - 28)

**Barbican Art Gallery.
Diaghilev: The Russian Years.**
Large exhibition of paintings, sculpture,
theatre design and costumes of Serge Diaghilev
in Russia and Europe until 1914 when he was
exiled from Russia.
Contact: 0171 638 5403. (Jan 25 - 12 Apr.*)

**LONDON ORIGINAL PRINT FAIR.**
Royal Academy of Arts.
Display and sale of original prints.
Contact: Miss Katherine Jones, 0171 439 7438.
(Mar. 16 - 25*)

**London Arts Season.**
Fabulous range of arts in multi-venue
programme of activities and entertainment.
Cinema 100 (previews, classic screenings
and special offers); Cezanne and
Leonardo Da Vinci exhibitions.
Contact: Barbara Brett 0171 814 5088.
(Feb. 1 - Mar. 31)

**Whitechapel Exhibition of Art.**
Works by German painter Emil Nolde,
(1867 - 1958). Whitechapel Art Gallery,
Whitechapel High Street, London E1.
Contact: Mark Slader 0171 377 5015.
(Feb. 1 - 21)

**Royal College of Art Exhibition:**
**A Century of Design.**
Largest exhibition ever staged by the
Royal College of Art in the Centenery of its
naming. Shows how College's design role
has helped shape 20th Century life.
Contact: Royal College of Art 0171 584 5020.
(Feb. 7 - Mar. 20)

**Cezanne Exhibition.**
Tate Gallery, Millbank, SWI. Part of the London
Arts Season. Possibly the most significant
exhibition of the artist's work ever shown.
Contact: LAS 0171 930 9663
or Tate Gallery 0171 887 8000. (Feb. 8 - Apr. 28)

**Roger de Grey, Painter.**
Exhibition at the Seckler Galleries,
Royal Academy of Arts, Piccadilly.
Contact: Press Office 0171 439 7438.
(Feb. 9 - Mar. 3)

**At Home with Constable's Cornfield.**
National Gallery, Trafalgar Square, WC2.
Exhibition based around the artist's Cornfield
and its reproductions in prints and other media
examining public response to the famous image.
Contact: National Gallery 0171 839 3321.
(Feb.14 - Apr. 21)

**Frederic, Lord Leighton 1830 - 1896.**
A Centennial Exhibition.
Royal Academy of Arts, Burlington House,
Piccadilly, London W1.
Contact: 0171 439 7438. (Feb. 16 - Apr. 21)

**Gustave Caillebotte 1848 - 1894.**
The Unknown Impressionist.
At the Seckler Galleries, Royal Academy
of Arts, Piccadilly, London.
Contact: 0171 439 7438. (Mar. 28 - June 23)

**David Livingstone and the Victorian Encounter**
**with Africa.**
Exhibition at the Wolfson Gallery, National
Portrait Gallery, St. Martin's Place, WC2.
Contact: 0171 306 0055. (Mar. 22 - June 23)

**Society of Women Artists Exhibition.**
Central Hall, Westminster. National and
international women artists are featured in
the major annual exhibition. Many works
in most media are for sale.
Contact: Central Hall 0171 222 8010.
(Mar. 22 - 30)

**Society of Botanical**
**Artists Exhibition.**
Central Hall, Westminster.
International exhibition with many works for sale.
Contact: Sue Burton 017496 74472.
(Apr. 19 - May 4)

**William Morris Centenery Exhibition.**
Victoria and Albert Museum, South Kensington.
The incredibly diverse world of Morris's
design from textiles and ceramics
to furniture and stained glass.
Contact: V & A 0171 938 8500. (May 8 - Sept. 1)

**The Cotswold Art Fair.**
Frogmill Inn, Nr Cheltenham, Gloucester.
Contact: Mrs. Caroline Penman 01444 482514.
(May 17 - 19)

**Degas as a Collector.**
Sunley Room, National Gallery, Trafalgar Square,
London WC2. To coincide with Degas
exhibition in the Gallery's Sainsbury Wing,
the artist's own collection of paintings,
drawings and prints will be displayed.
Contact: National Gallery 0171 839 3321.
(May 22 - Aug. 26)

**Barbican Art Gallery**
**- Eve Arnold: A Retrospective.**
Work by veteran American photojournalist and
Anglophile will be featured to coincide with
publication of her autobiography.
Contact: Barbican Centre 0171 638 5403.
(June 1* - August)

**Leon Kossoff Exhibition.**
Tate Gallery, Millbank, SW1.
Contact: 0171 887 8000. (June 6 - Sept. 2).

**Royal College of Art**
**1996 Degree Show.**
More than 25,000 people from industry,
media and public visit the most important
event in the College calendar featuring work
submitted by students for their finals.
Part One, Fine Art and Textiles (June 6 - 16),
Part Two, Applied Arts, Design (June 26 - July 7).
Contact: Royal College of Art 0171 584 5020.

**National Portrait Gallery:**
**BP Portrait Award.**
Exhibition at the Wolfson Gallery,
St. Martin's Place, WC2.
Contact: NPG 0171 306 0055.  (June*)

**Swan Arts Fair.**
Tetsworth, Oxfordshire.
Sale of paintings, prints and other works.
Contact: Caroline Penman 01444 483514.
(Aug. 30 - Sept. 1)

**Scottish National Portrait Gallery.**
Edinburgh. Richard and Maria Cosway:
Regency Artists of Taste and Fashion exhibition.
Contact: SNPG 0131 556 8921.
(Aug. 11 - Oct. 22)

**The Twentieth Century:**
**The Age of Modern Art.**
Royal Academy of Arts, Piccadilly,
London W1.  Major exhibition.
Contact 0171 439 7438. (Sept. 19 - Dec. 15)

**Peter Blake:**
**Associate Artist at the National Gallery.**
Exhibition showing the work produced by
Blake during his two years in the
National Gallery.  The Sunley Room, NG,
Trafalgar Square, London WC2.
Contact: National Gallery 0171 839 3321.
(Sept. 25 - Jan. 5, '97)

**Erwin Blumenfeld (1897 - 1969).**
One of the leading figures in the history
of photography.  His extraordinary innovation is
shown - from Vogue fashion shots to New York
down-and-outs. At the Barbican Art Gallery.
Contact: 0171 638 5403.  (Sept.1* - Dec.*)

**Armoury House Art Fair.**
Hon. Royal Artillery Headquarters,
City Road, London. Dealers in varying art
disciplines in popular art fair.
Contact: Mrs. Caroline  Penman 014440 482514.
(Oct. 16 - 18)

**Making & Meaning:**
**Rubens's Landscapes.**
The National Gallery holds the most outstanding
group of the artist's landscapes in the world.
Exhibition examines technique and motivation.
National Gallery, Trafalgar Square, London WC2.
Contact: National Gallery 0171 839 3321.
(Oct. 17 - Jan. 19, '97)

**Tate Gallery:  The Grand Tour Exhibition.**
Millbank, SW1. Contact: 0171 887 8000.
(Oct. 19 - Jan. 6)

**Hay Festival of Literature.**
Poetry and Literature.
Writers, lectures and events at Hay on Wye.
Contact: Festival Office 01497 821299.
(May 24 - June 1)

**LONDON INTERNATIONAL BOOKFAIR.**
Olympia, London. International trade event
covering all aspects of book publishing serving
publishers and booksellers as well as literary
agents and book buyers. In 1995 there were
925 companies from 35 countries represented.
Contact: 0181 948 9828. (Mar. 17 - 19)

**Bath International**
**Literature Festival.**
The story in written and oral form
at various venues includes readings
and creative workshops.
Contact: Bath Festival Trust 01225 462231.
(Feb. 24 - Mar. 3)

**Guildford Book Festival.**
Authors, poets, literary talks and lunches.
Children's events.
Contact:  Arts Administrator 01483 259167.
(Oct. 25 - Nov. 2)

**The Daily Telegraph Cheltenham Festival of Literature.**
Readings and lectures by leading
figures in literature as well as book
exhibitions and play-readings.
Contact: Festival Office 01242 521621.  (Oct.*)

**Rochester Dickens Festival.**
Larger celebration of their local author.
Displays, exhibitions and street entertainment
reflecting characters created by Dickens.
Contact: Rochester Tourist Information Centre
01634 843666.  (June 30 - July 2)

**Broadstairs Dickens Festival.**
Country fair, music, a play and
garden party - at various town venues.
Contact: Festival Organiser 01843 863453.
(June - July*)

**Midsummer Poetry Festival.**
Victoria Embankment Gardens, WC2.
Contact: Alternative Arts 0171 375 0441.
(June 16)

**Listowel Writer's Week, Eire.**
Contact: Ms Catherine FitzGerald
00 353 68 21074.
(May 15 - 19)

**Eastside Bookfair.**
Old Spitalfields Market, London E1.
Contact: Alternative Arts 0171 375 0441.
(Oct. 5 - 6)

# AVIATION

**Fighter Meet '96.**
North Weald Airfield, Epping, Essex.
Europe's leading fighter aircraft show.
Contact: Fighter Meet Ltd. 0181 866 9993.
(May 11 - 12)

**Air Fete.**
RAF Mildenhall, Bury St. Edmunds, Suffolk.
Military aircraft from NATO countries and
elsewhere converge for one of Europe's
largest air displays.
Contact: Fete Office 01638 823211.
(May 25 - 26)

**Middle Wallop International
Air Show '96.**
Army Air Corps Centre attracts
international entries and visitors.
Contact: International Air Show
Office 01264 384461.
(June 15 - 16)

### The DHL Biggin Hill International Airfair and Helifest.

Biggin Hill, Kent. Two-day aviation feast of military and commericial aircraft, including historic aircraft flights.
Contact: James Maitland, Air Displays International 01959 572277. (June 8 - 9*)

### Yeovilton International Air Display.

Royal Naval Air Station Yeovilton, Ilchester, Somerset. Major international air display and museum. Contact: RNAS Yeovilton 01935 840551. (July 13)

### Farnborough Aerospace Exhibition and Air Show.

Flying displays and aircraft from around the world in the plane spotters event-of-the-year. Contact: Air Show Office 0171 938 3666. (Sept. 2 - 8*)

### Battle of Britain Open Day.

Biggin Hill Airport, Kent.
Displays by historic and wartime aircraft including the Spitfire. Contact: Air Displays International 01959 572277. (Sept. 17)

### Jersey Air Rally.

Private aircraft from all over the UK and France converge of the Channel Island for a flier's get-together.
Contact: Jersey Tourism 01534 500700. (May 3 - 5)

## CEREMONIAL & MILITARY

### TROOPING THE COLOUR.

The Queen's Official Birthday Parade.
Horse Guards Parade, Whitehall, London SW1. Tradition, pageantry, colour as massed bands and troops parade. The Queen takes the salute. Stand tickets by invitation only but plenty of room to watch the parade of the Ist Bttn Irish Guards. Contact: HQ Household Division 0171 414 2357. (June 15)

### Charles I Commemoration.

The King's Army in 17th Century dress parade from St. James's Palace to Banqueting House, Whitehall, London SW1. (Jan. 28*)

**Changing of the Guard.**
Daily - see separate section.

**Ceremony of the Keys.**
Daily - see separate section.

**Celebration of HM The Queen's
Accession to the Throne.**
41-gun salute by The King's Troop,
Royal Horse Artillery at Hyde Park
(opposite Dorchester Hotel) at Noon
and a 62-gun salute by the
Hon. Artillery Company at the Tower of London at
1pm. Contact: Tower of London 0171 709 0765.
(Feb. 6)

Gun Salutes are fired at the same time to
celebrate the following occasions: The Queen's
Birthday: April 21. The Anniversary of the
Coronation: June 3. HM Queen Elizabeth The
Queen Mother's Birthday: August 4. Prince
Philip's 75th Birthday: June 10. Salutes are never
fired on a Sunday. Additional salutes take place
for Trooping the Colour, the State Opening of
Parliament and State Visits. *See separate section
on Changing The Guard.*

**Edinburgh Military Tattoo.**
World-famous event. Military colour,
pageantry and precision as troops, pipes and
bands parade under floodlight on the ramparts
of historic Edinburgh Castle. Contact: Tattoo
Office 0131 225 1188. (Aug. 2 - 24)

**Tower of London Easter Sunday
State Parade and Church Service.**
"Beefeaters" lead dignitaries and invited
guests to service in Tower Chapel.
Contact: Tower of London: 0171 709 0765.
(Apr. 7)

**Beating Retreat
by the Household Division.**
Horse Guards Parade, SW1.
Floodlit ceremony with trumpeters
and massed bands of the Household
Cavalry - over 400 musicians - on parade.
Contact: Public Information Office,
HQ London District 0171 414 2357.
(June 5 - 6)

**Sounding Retreat.**
Royal Marines, Horse Guards Parade, SW1.
Massed Bands, pageantry and tradition.
Contact: Public Information Office,
HQ London District 0171 414 2357.
(June 11, 12 & 14).

**The Garter Ceremony.**
The Queen accompanies Knights of the
Garter (Her Majesty's Personal Award)
through Windsor Castle for their annual service.
Contact: Windsor Castle 01753 868286.
(June 17*)

# The Royal Family. Having a jolly good time with your Royal favourite.

**By Philip Dampier (Britain's leading Royal watcher).**

It is a summer pastime as traditional as Wimbledon's strawberries and cream - spotting a member of the Royal Family during "The Season."

Gone are the days when you could rely on them to be in the same place at the same time every year.

As Royal marriages have crumbled and hoardes from John Major's "classless society" have moved in on events like Ascot and Henley, the social diaries have been transformed.

Each member of "The Firm" as Prince Philip calls the Monarchy, now goes his or her own way in pursuit of happiness. Never again will we see Princess Diana and the Duchess of York poke friends with umbrellas as they once did at Ascot.

But, armed with the inside knowledge and the right uniform, it is still possible to - literally - rub shoulders with the Royals.

So here is a brief guide on where to spot your favourite:

THE QUEEN MOTHER'S summer always revolves around racing. She can always be seen at Royal Ascot, the Derby and the Cheltenham National Hunt Festival. Spontaneous applause often breaks out as she walks to inspect the horses before a big race. Her now familiar appearance outside Clarence House on her August 4 birthday is now also an integral part of the social scene. She is now a very old lady and we can only hope she will be with us for some years yet.

THE QUEEN AND PRINCE PHILIP also attend the races, although the Duke of Edinburgh spends much of the time at Royal Ascot watching test matches on the Royal Box television set! He loves cricket and, together with the Queen, always attends the Lord's Test when the players are presented to them.

Last year, Prince Philip was the only British royal to attend Cowes Week on the Isle of Wight in July-August. The event has been sadly lacking in glamour of late and plans to scrap the Royal Yacht Britannia will not help.

However, wander round the Windsor Horse Trials, the Chelsea Flower Show and top polo matches at Windsor and you could easily bump into the Queen or Prince Philip.

PRINCESS DIANA is now the wild card of the Season. Once a regular at Ascot, Wimbledon and polo matches to watch Prince Charles, she is now totally unpredictable. For the last two years, she has attended Wimbledon only on Men's Finals day, being a great fan of Pete Sampras. But she has also turned up at the pre-Wimbledon Stella Artois Tournament at Queen's Club in West London.

Do not expect to see her at any horsey gatherings again. She hates racing!

However, she might well arrive at the British Grand Prix at Silverstone - usually accompanied by sons, Wills and Harry.

PRINCE CHARLES never goes to Wimbledon. But he does give the appearance of attending the

Derby and Royal Ascot, mainly out of courtesy to his parents and the Queen Mother. But he often sneaks away after just one or two races to play polo!

He can also be seen at the Trooping the Colour ceremony with the rest of the Royals for the Queen's official birthday - and at the Royal Highland Games at Braemar.

As social habits change and Royal preferences widen, so new events now seem to be considered as an integral part of the Season - almost all the year round!

For example, Rugby Union internationals are now regarded as great social gatherings, with groaning hampers being opened in car parks hours before kick-off time. Green Wellingtons, Range Rovers and loud voices are the order of the day here. The Royals have taken rugby to their hearts.

PRINCESS ANNE, suitably dressed in tartan, has become Scotland's Royal patron. PRINCE EDWARD fills a similar role at England matches and PRINCESS DIANA is a regular at Cardiff Arms Park for the Welsh games, to which she normally travels by train along with Wills and Harry.

DIANA also has an interest in England but she tends not to attend their matches, so as not to offend the Welsh.

PRINCESS ANNE's Scottish connections extend to her regular attendance - along with second husband Tim Laurence - at the Royal Caledonian Ball in London's Grosvenor Park Hotel in April. And, being a former Olympic horsewoman, she can often be spotted at various horse trials, chatting to Tim - and her first husband, Captain Mark Phillips.

PRINCE ANDREW, as a serving Royal Navy officer, is more elusive. But he has caught the golf bug (trying to get a single-figure handicap!) and is now a regular at The Open Championship and other tournaments. As for his estranged (but still good friends) wife, the DUCHESS OF YORK, you stand just as much chance of seeing her in Bali, Barcelona, Boston or Bermuda as you do of catching her at home!

**Royal Tournament.**
Earls Court, SW5. Pageantry, spectacle, military precision - and fun at all-services showpiece in aid of service charities.
Contact: Sarah Cater 0171 370 8202.
(July 9 - 20)

**BUCKINGHAM PALACE.**
Open to the public during August and September. Dates to be announced.
Contact: Buckingham Palace 0171 930 4832.

**STATE OPENING OF PARLIAMENT.**
The Queen, usually accompanied by Prince Charles, rides in State with mounted escort of the Household Cavalry from Buckingham Palace to the Houses of Parliament to formally open the Parliamentary session and to read the traditional Queen's Speech announcing the proposals of HM Government. (Nov.*)

**Trafalgar Day Parade.**
Sea Cadets parade to commemorate the anniversary of Lord Nelson's victory at the Battle of Trafalgar on October 21, 1805.
Contact: Sea Cadets Association 0171 928 8978.
(Oct.*)

### Remembrance Day Service and Parade.

Cenotaph, SW1. The nation respects two minutes' silence at 11 am in honour of the dead of two World Wars. The Queen and members of the Royal Family join government, service and diplomatic officials in wreath-laying. (Nov. 10)

### The Lord Mayor's Procession and Show.

City of London. Marching bands and floats parade from Guildhall to the Royal Courts of Justice celebrating the innauguration of the new Lord Mayor. Fireworks at dusk best seen from Westminster Bridge.
Contact: City of London PR 0171 606 3030. (Nov. 13*)

## CHARITY BALLS & FUNCTIONS

### Queen Charlotte's Birthday Ball.

Grosvenor House, Park Lane, London W1. Major event in the traditional social Season. Queen Charlotte Hospital's major fund-raising event.
Contact: Birthday Ball Office 0181 741 4653. (Sept.*)

### ROYAL CALEDONIAN BALL.

Grosvenor House, Park Lane, London W1. Premier social event in aid of Scottish charities.
Contact: Mrs. Roger Tym 01264 810363. (May 2)

### The Tartan Ball.

The Honourable Artillery Company, Armoury House, City Road, London EC1.
In aid of Children with Leukaemia.
Contact: Suzanne Macrae 0171 404 0808. (Apr. 19*)

### Chelsea Young League Disco.

Savoy Hotel, Strand, London WC2.
In aid of the NSPCC.
Contact: Lesley Edwards 0171 336 7738. (Jan. 3)

### Maple Leaf Charity Ball.

Grosvenor House, Park Lane, London W1.
Contact: 0171 499 6363. (Feb. 8)

### JESTER BALL.

Grosvenor House, Park Lane, London W1.
In aid of Action on Addiction.
Contact: Rachel Virden 0171 793 1011. (May 9*)

### The Royal Marsden Ball.

In support of the Royal Marsden Hospital. Location to be confirmed.
Contact: Simon Gold 0181 341 7286. (May 17)

### Gulls Eggs City Luncheon.

Livery company members and businessmen at Skinners' Hall, EC4, for light charity lunch with the "rare delicacy" of gulls eggs.
Contact: Sally Walton 0171 581 9225. (May 21)

**May Golf Day.**
The Brendan Blake Classic - at Ealing.
In aid of The Royal Marsden Hospital.
Contact: Simon Gold 0181 341 7286.  (May 22)

**Great Celebrity Tie
and Scarf Auction.**
In aid of Cancer Relief at Bonham's,
Montpelier Street, London SW7.
Contact: Carella McGregor 0171 887 8249. (Oct.*)

**The Creative Ball.**
Grosvenor House, Park Lane.
Contact: 0171 499 6363.  (Dec. 1*)

**NSPCC Cinderella Ball.**
Savoy Hotel, Strand, London WC2.
Contact: Jane Woodfield,
London Events 0171 336 7738.  (Nov.*)

**Lifeboat & Mermaid Ball.**
London Hilton in aid of RNLI.
Contact: Mrs. Sue Clifton 0171 834 5264.  (Dec*)

**Magdelene College May Ball.**
Cambridge, in aid of The Prince's Trust.
Contact: Miss Anna Norman 01223 328042.
(June*)

**Midsummer's Ball.**
The Savoy Hotel.
In aid of Cancer Relief  Macmillan Fund.
Contact: Sally Walton 0171 581 9225.  (June*)

**The Midsummer Ball.**
London Hilton, Park Lane.
Unique black-tie event created by Hotel's
management to raise funds for charity.
Contact: Sandra Lane 0171 208 4045. (June 24)

**Blenheim Palace Gala Evening.**
Oxfordshire, in aid of
Cancer Research Campaign.
Contact: Mrs. Trivia Birchley 01923 283770.
(June*)

**Gentleman and Players Summer Ball.**
Dorchester Hotel, London W1.
In aid of the NSPCC.
Contact: Jane Woodfield 0171 336 7738.  (June*)

**Windsor Race Night Auction.**
Bidding is followed by Dinner.
In aid of Children with Leukaemia.
Contact: Taryn Bennellick 0171 731 8199.
(July 22)

**Wellington Ball.**
In aid of Cancer Relief Macmillan Fund at the
Cavalry and Guards Club, 127 Piccadilly.
Contact: Catherine O'Kelly  0171 581 9225.
(Oct.*)

**Sotheby's Charity Auction.**
Dinner and auction room fun.
In aid of Cancer Relief Macmillan Fund.
Contact: Sally Walton 0171 581 9225.  (Oct. 9*)

**Help the Aged Gold Awards Luncheon.**
London Hilton, Park Lane.
Contact: Help the Aged Special Events 0171 253
2926.  (Nov*)

**Breast Cancer Campaign Ball.**
Waldorf Hotel, W1.
Contact: Helen Sandwell 0171 430 1013.  (Nov*)

**Barnardo Ball.**
The Savoy Hotel in aid of Barnado's charity.
Contact: Mrs. William Pull 0171 602 7833. (Nov*)

**The Royal Star
and Garter Winter Ball.**
Park Lane Hotel. In support of Disabled Sailors,
Soldiers and Airmen.
Contact: David Burland 0181 948 8865. (Nov*)

**The Fall Ball.**
The Grosvenor House Hotel.
In aid of Age Concern.
Contact: Miss Lucy Colyer-Jordan
0181 679 8000. (Nov*)

**Charity Greyhound Evening.**
Wimbledon Stadium in aid of the
Breast Cancer Campaign.
Contact:  Helen Sandwell 0171 439 1013.  (April)

**Champagne Reception.**
The Guards Museum, London SW1.
In aid of the Royal Marsden League of Friends.
Contact: Simon Gold 0171 730 4092. (March)

**Royal Academy's**
**Summer Exhibition Private View.**
In aid of Help the Aged.
Contact: Special Events 0171 253 2926. (Aug.*)

**Late Summer Dance.**
The Hurlingham Club. In aid of Royal
Marsden Junior League of Friends.
Contact: Simon Gold 0171 928 7788. (Sept.)

**Night of the Stars Ball.**
Grosvenor House, Park Lane.
In aid of Children with Leukaemia.
Contact: 0171 731 8199. (Oct)

## CHILDREN'S ACTIVITIES & EVENTS

**Children's Fashion and Tea Party.**
The Savoy Hotel. In aid of Cancer
Relief Macmillan Fund.
Contact: Charlotte Holmes 0171 887 8249.
(Mar. 11)

**Natural History Museum.**
Meet the Nature Detectives feature.
Contact: Natural History Museum 0171 938 9388.
(March 15*)

**The Amazing Great Children's Party.**
The British Genius Site, Battersea Park,
London SW8. In aid of The Foundation for
Children with Leukaemia.
Contact: Suzanna Macrae 0171 404 0808. (July*)

**Teddy Bears Picnic.**
Battersea Park, London. If you go down to SW11
today, you're sure of a big surprise. Proud Teddy
owners, young and not so young, gather there for
one of the biggest bears meetings in the world.
Contact: Joan Fulton 0181 871 8107. (Aug. 4)

**The Teddy Bear Fair.**
Alexandra Palace, London N22. After the
Picnic, another chance for Teddy-lovers
to indulge in toy bearland.
Contact: Alexandra Palace 0181 365 2121.
(Nov. 8 - 9*)

**Disney On Ice Spectacular.**
Mickey, Minnie, Donald and Pluto are all there
at the three-weeks ice show at Wembley Arena.
Contact: Wembley Arena 0181 902 8833.
(Oct. 14*)

**Punch and Judy Festival.**
Covent Garden, London WC2.
Contact: Prof. Percy Press 0181 802 4656.
(Oct.*)

**Billy Smart's Circus.**
Old Deer Park, Richmond.
Contact: Arts Section: 0181 331 0534. (Oct. *)

**The Dolls House Fair.**
Alexandra Palace, London N22.
Fascinating collections of miniaturised houses
including such small detail as cutlery and
matching upholstery.
Contact: Alexandra Palace 0181 365 212.
(Nov. 9*)

**Peter Rabbit Children's Party.**
Holy Trinity Church Hall, London SW3.
In aid of I Can Charity.
Contact: Karen Horn 0171 374 4422. (June*)

**Children's Concert.**
In the grounds of Polesdon Lacey,
the Regency house now operated by the
National Trust near Great Bookham, Surrey.
Contact: Eloise Harris 01372 453401. (June 16)

**Covent Garden Mayfayre**
**and Puppet Festival.**
St. Paul's Church Gardens, Bedford Street, WC2.
Celebrating Samuel Pepys visit in 1662.
Contact: Alternative Arts 0171 375 0441. (May 12)

# CHRISTMAS & NEW YEAR

**Christmas Cocktail Fair.**
In aid of Save The Children Fund.
The Banqueting House, Whitehall.
Contact: STC Charity Events 0171 703 5400.
(Dec.*)

**Trafalgar Square Christmas Tree.**
Each year the Norwegian people present a
Christmas tree to the British people as a sign
of friendship and thanks for help given to
Norway during the Second World War.
Carols are sung beneath its decorated
boughs and it even survives the excesses of
New Year's Eve celebrations in the Square.
(Nov. - Jan. 6)

**Christmas Lights.**
Free nightly spectacle - display of festive lights.
Contact: Oxford Street Association
0171 629 1234. Regent Street Association
0171 491 4429.  Bond Street Association
0171 629 1682. Also Covent Garden
Christmas Lights.  (Nov. 3* - Jan 6)

**Christmas Market.**
Duchess of Kent to open major Christmas event
in aid of Cancer Relief MacMillan Fund at Royal
Horticultural Society Hall, Westminster. Frenzy of
purchases - plus ticket-only Preview - helped
raise £135,000 for the charity last year.
Contact: Charlotte Holmes 0171 887 8249.
(Nov.11 - 12)

**Carol Concert.**
Royal Naval College Chapel, Greenwich.
Contact: Organiser 0181 317 868767. (Dec. 5)

**Carol Concert.**
Guards Chapel, Wellington Barracks.
(invitation only) In aid of British Heart Foundation.
Contact: BHF Fund Raising 0171 935 0185.
(Dec.*)

**Carol Concert.**
Royal guest expected at annual Christmas
event at Guards Museum, Wellington Barracks.
Martyn Lewis introduces celebrities.
Reception follows. In aid of Cancer Relief
Macmillan Fund.
Contact: Catherine O'Kelly  0171 581 9225.
(Dec. 11)

**Carol Concert.**
Guildhall, City of London.
In aid of the Royal British Legion.
Contact: Julia Maude 0171 973 0637.  (Dec.*)

**The Festive Table
& Christmas Craft Fair.**
Alexandra Palace, N22. Exhibition of Christmas
goods featuring seasonal food and drink.
Contact:  Mike Nugent 0181 366 3153.
(Nov. 29 - Dec. 1*)

### Great Christmas Pudding Race.
Covent Garden Piazza, WC2. Yuletide fun amid the street entertainers of "The Garden". In aid of Cancer Research Campaign. Contact: Campaign Events 0181 446 4226. (Dec.*)

### Boxing Day: Peter Pan Cup Swimming Race.
Serpentine, Hyde Park, W2.
Hardy swimmers brave the elements and hypothermia for a post-Christmas Day dip. Contact: Mr. Titmus 01753 544441. (Dec. 26)

### Boxing Day.
Packs of foxhounds gather in towns many parts of the country for the traditional Boxing Day Meets. (Dec. 26)

### Allendale Baal Festival.
Costumed local people parade with burning barrels of tar on their heads to celebrate the New Year. Market Square, Allendale, Northumberland. (Dec. 31)

### New Year's Eve Celebrations.
Trafalgar Square. Thousands cram the centre of London and often the fountains of Trafalgar Square to see out the old and see in the new. (Dec. 31)

### Evening Standard 1996 London Parade.
Tenth anniversary of spectacular event, the biggest of its kind in Europe, which attracts nearly one million people to the streets of the capital. Giant inflatable cartoon characters - seven storeys high - marching bands, cheerleaders, clowns, acrobats, vintage cars and floats to welcome in the New Year. Westminster and West End.
Contact: Lynne Parker 0181 744 0811. (Jan. 1)

### Hogmanay.
First-footing and more than a wee dram to welcome in '96 at the giant Edinburgh Street party. Live music, carnival, street theatre and a MacMultitude of events to welcome in 1997. Contact: Barry Wright,
Unique Events, 0131 557 3990.
(Dec 31 - Jan. 1)

### Llanfarian New Year Sheepdog Trials.
Get rid of that hangover in the fresh air of the Welsh countryside. Join the proud owners and their dogs at the annual, bracing start to the New Year at Llanfarian, Aberystwyth, Dyfed. Contact:  J. B. Jones 01970 617590.  (Jan. 1)

## COMPUTER, CONSUMER & INFORMATION TECHNOLOGY

### National Computer Shopper Show.
NEC, Birmingham. The incredible advances in computer technology for all to see. Contact: Blenheim Events 0181 742 2628. (March 14 - 17)

### MEMS '96.
Latest electronic music and recording equipment for you to try out and buy. Top industry gurus on hand at Olympia Exhibition Centre. Contact: Future Events 01225 442244. (Apr. 19 - 21)

**Cable & Satellite.**
The European Broadcasting and Communication Show (Trade), National Hall, Olympia. Contact: Reed Exhibition Companies 0181 910 7910. (April*)

**Environmental Technology.**
NEC, Birmingham (Trade). UK's leading enviro-equipment and services exhibition. Contact: Reed Exhibition Companies 0181 910 7910. (Apr. 13 - 15*)

**Home PC Show.**
Olympia. The PC as home office, children's educational aid, executive ally or the disc-game addictor! Fun day for all the family. Contact: Real Time Events Ltd. 0181 849 6200. (May 30 - June 2)

## COUNTRY PURSUITS AND FOLK CRAFTS

**International Shooting Sports Association.**
NEC, Birmingham. Weapons, ammunition, equipment including advice and shooting holidays. Contact: Linc Exhibitions 01733 558900. (Apr. 19 - 21)

**Angling Exhibition.**
NEC, Birmingham. Not only rods, reels and bait but celebrities, advice and fishing-clinics. Contact: Linc Exhibitions 01733 558900. (Apr. 19 - 21)

**Chatsworth Angling Fair.**
Chatsworth House, Bakewell, Derbyshire. Rods from around the world at this major international angling event. Contact: Andrew Cuthbert 01328 830367. (May11 - 12)

**Charity Clay Pigeon Shoot.**
In aid of Action on Addiction. Popular event - location to be announced. Contact: Rachel Virden 0171 793 1011. (May 18)

**Living Crafts.**
Hatfield House, Hatfield, Herts. 700 craftsmen and women demonstrate their skills. Contact: Jean Younger 01582 761235. (May*)

**Countrywide Workshops Fair.**
Mount Ephraim, Faversham, Kent. Display of traditional crafts and near-forgotten skills. Proceeds used in support of 65 workshops. Contact: Valerie Wood-Gaiger 01722 326886. (May 15 - 16)

**Woburn Abbey Angling Fair.**
Superb location for popular fair for fishing fans. Contact: Andrew Cuthbertson 01328 830367. (June 8 - 9)

**Irish National Sheepdog Trials.**
Markethill,Co. Armagh. One of five major Sheepdog Trials held in Britain and Ireland each year. Contact: International Sheepdog Society 01234 352672. (July 25 - 27)

**Grouse shooting season begins.**
(Aug. 12)

**Chatsworth Country Fair.**
Chatsworth House, near Bakewell, Derbyshire. Contact: Andrew Cuthbertson 01328 830367. (Aug. 31 - Sept. 1)

**Egremont Crab Fair.**
Greasy-pole races and the legendary Gurning - ugly face-pulling - feature along with traditional events at the Crab Fair. Contact: Mr. W. Rickerby 01946 820376. (Sept 21)

**Pheasant shooting begins.** (Oct 1)

**Nottingham Goose Fair.**
Forest Recreation Ground, Nottingham.
Traditional English Fair, arguably the oldest but
with up-to-date amusements including funfair.
Contact: Fair Office 0115 941 7324. (Oct. 4 - 6)

**Crafts and Countryside
Come to Town.**
National Trust event at
Morden Hall Park, Morden, Surrey.
Contact: Eloise Harris 01372 453401.  (May 6)

## CUSTOMS

**Jorvik Festival.**
Lively festival celebrating Viking culture including
torchlight processions, longboat races, concerts
and firework displays in various North Yorkshire
venues including York.  Contact: Festival Office
01904 611944. (Feb 10 - 17)

**Town Crier Championships.**
Oyez, Oyez, pray give your attendance at the
Realm's principal event to find the Crier of the
Year from the Loyal Company of Town Criers.
Date and venue to be confirmed. Contact: Ted
Davy, Town Crier Beadle 01507 466063. (April)

**Ann Boleyn Memorial.**
Each year a basket of red roses is placed on Ann
Boleyn's burial site at the Tower of London on the
anniversary of her death on May 19, 1536.
(May19)

**World Dock Pudding Championship.**
Mytholmroyd, Hebden Bridge, West Yorkshire.
Battle of the Puds as contestants compete to
produce traditional puddings judged for taste,
consistency and presentation.
Contact: Mrs. Sandra Wickham 01422 823630.
(May 19)

**Ceremony of the Lillies and the Roses.**
Tower of London. In private ceremony,
representatives place Eton lillies and
Kings College roses on the spot where
Henry VI - founder of the two seats of
learning - was murdered in 1471.
(May 21)

**Eton's Fourth of June celebration.**
"The Eton Boating Song" is sung heartily
by boys during day of celebration culminating
in a parade of boats on the Thames.
Contact: Bursar's Office, Eton College,
Windsor, Berkshire 01752 671000.  (June 3).

**Appleby Horse Fair.**
Gypsies and travellers travel to Appleby
in Cumbria for the traditional annual
meeting and sale of horses.
Contact: Appleby-in-Westmorland
Tourist Centre 01768 351177. (June 6 - 12)

**Pearly King and Queens
Harvest Festival Service.**
St Martin in the Fields, WC2.
Pearly Kings and Queens in traditional
cockney costermongers attire. (Oct.*)

**Beating the Bounds.**
Tower of London.  Warders and Choristers mark
the boundaries. In olden days boys were beaten
at points marking the boundary.  Today the
marking points are beaten by the boys.
Provisionally Ascension Day.
Contact: Tower of London 0171 709 0765.

**Gold Panning Championships.**
Not exactly The Yukon, but the Dolancothi
Goldmines at Llanwrda in Dyfed attract the
equivalent of the Forty Niners trying their
luck at panning for gold.
Contact:  Dolancothi Goldmines
01558 650359.  (July)

**Thames Barrier.**
Full tidal closure, Eastmoor Street, Woolwich SE7.
A new custom for Londoners witnessing the full
closure of the engineering marvel, built to prevent
flooding of the capital.  (Oct. *)

**Sea Shanty Festival.**
Hull Marina, Humberside. Songs handed down by sailors for hundreds of years feature among music celebrating the maritime history of Hull.
Contact: Hull Tourism 01482 595726.
(Sept. 5 - 8)

**Spitalfields Pancake Day Race.**
Between 20 and 50 teams of four run 100-yard relays tossing pancakes.
Politicians, pub teams and office workers test their skills against pancake-hardened veterans.
Contact: Maggie Pinhorn,
Alternative Art, 0171 375 0441. (Shrove Tuesday)

**Buxton Well Dressing Festival and Carnival.**
Buxton, Derbyshire.
An ancient ceremony, dating from pagan times. Pictures, made from flower petals, are placed on wells around the Peak District town.
Contact: High Peak Borough 01298 23114.
(July 10 - 13)

## DANCE AND DRAMA

**London International Mime Festival.**
South Bank and various other venues including Battersea Arts Centre, Lavender Hill, London SW11. Theatre, children's and cabaret events.
Contact: Joseph Selig 0171 637 5661.
(Jan.12 - 26)

**British Open Ballroom & Latin American Dance Championships.**
Winter Gardens, Blackpool. Dancers travel from around the world for this annual event.
Contact: Festival Office 01253 25252.
(May 24 - 31)

**Aspects of Dance.**
The Wimbledon Theatre.
In aid of The Foundation for Children With Leukaemia. Performances covering wide range of disciplines and techniques.
Contact: Suzanna Macrae 0171 404 0808.

**Gwyl Ifan Festival.**
The largest Welsh Folk Dancing Festival at venues around Cardiff.
Contact: Dai Jones 01222 563989.
(June 21 - 23)

**Harwich Festival.**
The East Coast port celebrates with folk dancing, concerts and exhibitions.
Contact: A. Bartholomew. 1 High Cross House, Main Road, Harwich, Essex CO12 3LP.
(June 29 - July 7)

**Galway Arts Festival.**
Including country and formal Irish dance.
Contact: Fergal McGrath 00 353 91 583800.
(July 14 - 28)

**Dance Umbrella.**
Different venues in the capital.
Contact: Dance Umbrella 0181 741 4040.
(Oct. 12 - 13*)

**Open Dance Festival.**
Victoria Embankment Gardens, Villiers Street, WC2. Contact: Alternative Arts 0171 375 0441.
(June 1 - 2)

**Thirtieth Brighton International Festival of Performing Arts.**
Annual event featuring all aspects of the performing arts.
Contact: Ms Lisa Wolfe 01273 676926.
(May 4 - 26)

## EQUESTRIAN

**BADMINTON INTERNATIONAL HORSE TRIALS.**
Avon. World-class Three-Day Event: showjumping, cross-country and dressage.
Contact: Jane Gundry, Show Administration 01454 218272. (May 2 - 5)

**ROYAL WINDSOR HORSE SHOW.**
Home Park, Windsor Castle, Berkshire.
Displays by Cavalry, RN, Kings Troop
and fireworks display in the Queen's
favourite back garden.
Contact: Showground 01753 860633.
(May 8 - 12)

**London Harness Horse Easter Parade.**
Battersea Park, London SW11.
Contact: Battersea Park 0181 871 7540.
(Apr. 7 - 8*)

**Richmond Horse Show.**
Old Deer Park, Richmond. Contact: Richmond
Sports Services 0181 941 0485. (May 24 - 26)

**HICKSTEAD.**
The All-England Jumping Course, Hickstead,
West Sussex, is the home to three major
showjumping events. The Nations Cup (June*),
the Royal International Horse Show (July*), and
the four-day Silk Cut Derby (August*).
Contact: Marathon Event
Management 0181 366 3153.

**Calor Gas British Open Championships.**
Gatcombe Park, Stroud, Glos.. World class
showjumpers attempt one of the toughest and
most spectacular courses in jumping.
Contact: 0181 742 2169. (Aug.*)

**Bramham Three-Day Horse Trials.**
Near Wetherby, Yorkshire.
Contact: British Horse Society
Trials Office: 01203 696762.
(June 6 - 9)

**Millstreet International Horse Show.**
Co. Cork, Eire.
Contact: Thomas Duggan 00 353 29 70039.
(July 30 - Aug. 4)

**Blair Castle Three-Day Horse Trials.**
Contact: 01796 481207.
(Aug. 29 - Sept. 1)

**Kerrygold Dublin Horse Show.**
Royal Dublin Showground.
Contact: Shane Cleary 00 353 1 668 0866.
(Aug. 6 - 10*)

**Burghley Three-Day Horse Trials.**
Burghley House, Stamford, Lincolnshire.
One of the major events in the equestrian
calendar. Contact: Trials Office 01780 52131.
(Sept. 5 - 8)

**BLENHEIM PALACE HORSE TRIALS.**
Blenheim Palace, Woodstock, Oxfordshire.
One of the country's principle international
three-day equestrian events.
Contact: Blenheim Palace Horse Trials
01993 8133335. (Sept.)

**Tweseldown Novice Horse Trials.**
Tweseldown Racecourse, Fleet, Hampshire.
Contact: 01252 616731. (Sept.)

**Osberton Horse Trials.**
Worksop, Nottingham.
Contact: Estate Office 01909 472206. (Sept.)

**Horse of the Year Show.**
Wembley Arena, Empire Way, Wembley.
Annual indoor extravaganza attracting
the world's top showjumpers.
Contact: Jane Williams, British Showjumping
Centre 01203 693088. (Oct. 19 - 22)

**Horsemen's Sunday.**
St. John's Church, Hyde Park Crescent, W2.
Contact: Ross Nye 0171 262 3791. (Sept.*)

**Tattersalls Newmarket Yearling Sales.**
Park Paddocks, Newmarket. Mix with top
owners, buyers, agents and racing folk
bidding for some of the best-bred bloodstock in
the world. Contact: Tattersalls Ltd.
01638 665931. (Oct.*)

**British Equine Event.**
Royal Agricultural Society specialist show
at the National Agricultural Centre,
Stoneleigh Park, Warwickshire.
Contact: Show Organiser 01203 696969.
(Nov. 3 - 4*)

## International
## Showjumping Championships.

Olympia, W14. Major annual international indoor equestrian event. Contact: Ms V Bull, Philbeach Events 0171 370 8206. (Dec. 18 - 22)

## POLO SEASON opens in May.

Major centres:

Guards Polo Club, Smith's Lawn, Windsor Great Park, Englefield Green, Egham, Surrey TW20 0HP. (01784 434212).

Cowdray Park Polo Club, Midhurst, West Sussex GU29 0AQ. (01730 813257).

Cirencester Park Polo Club, The Old Kennels, Cirencester Park, Gloucestershire GL7 1UB. (01285 653225).

*Fixtures are not available until shortly before the start of the season but the following events are expected:*

**May:** Gerald Balding Cup, Cirencester. Texaco Trophy final, Cowdray Park. Heats and Final of Dollar Cup, Cowdray Park. Alfred Dunhill Queen's Cup, Guards.

**June:** Warwickshire Cup, Cirencester. JAL Cup, Guards. Open Championship for Gold Cup, Cowdray Park. Cirencester 12-Goal Championship. British Open (June -July).

**July:** Jack Gammon Trophy final, Cowdray Park. Cowdray Park Challenge Cup Final, Cowdray Park. Prince Philip Trophy, Guards.

**August:** National 15 Championship, Cirencester.

Final of National Pony Club Championships, Cowdray Park. Cheltenham Cup, Cowdray. Kingscote Cup, Cirencester.

## HORSE DRIVING TRIALS.

*Fixtures are not announced until shortly before the Season. But the following dates are expected.*

**June:**

Castle Howard, Yorkshire. Tatton Park, Cheshire. Macallam Burgie, Forres, Morayshire. Sandringham, Norfolk.

**July:**

Normanhurst, East Sussex. Drumlanrig Castle, Dumfries. Streatham Park, Durham.

**August:**

British Open, Gatcombe Park, Glos. Godmersham Park, Kent. Seacliff, East Lothian. Cirencester, Glos.

**Sept:**

Burghley Remy Martin Horse Trials, Burghley House, Stamford, Lincs. National Horse Driving Championships, Windsor. Contact: British Horse Society 01203 696697.

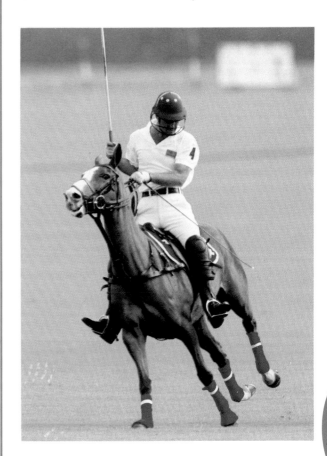

# The European Championship: We'll be ready for the best of the rest!

**By Terry Venables
(England manager & coach)**

I am really looking forward to this summer's European Cup Finals. The tournament promises to be one of the most closely fought of all time, with 15 of the best teams in the world taking part.

Yes, I said the world. Very well, some of the South American teams are good, very good. But remember that of the last eight in the World Cup, seven were European and that says something for the ever growing standard of European competition. Okay, the World Champions are Brazil, but they were the exception.

As far as England are concerned, we are quietly confident we can do very well. We have a strong pool of players to choose from, and those like David Platt and Paul Gascoigne, made even stronger, I feel, by experiencing the white heat of soccer in Italy.

Similarly, our domestic competitions in England have been made sharper by the arrival of world class foreigners in our leagues. Klinsmann, for example, set Spurs alight while he was there. Others have now followed and players like these give a richer quality to our game.

As a squad, England are progressing well. But we should not forget that teams from other countries are progressing, too. Gone are the days of a ten-nil result when you knew you could overrun the opposition with your eyes closed.

Now, soccer throughout Europe has dramatically improved, both from a technical and fitness standpoint. Players today are sharper, faster, more aware than they were only a few years ago.

That is why we have got to adapt our football to meet today's needs. We cannot go around playing at 100 mph all the time. We would be taken apart if we did. The style and pattern we play has to be adjusted for every game, tailor-made if you like to nullify the opponent's strengths and take advantage of his weaknesses. Similarly, we know they will adapt their game on the same basis.

When I first took over as England coach, it took some time, not surprisingly, for the players to grasp exactly what I wanted from them. Most of them have now got the message and the more the squad trains together, the better things will become.

And that brings me to another point - England squad training. After years of coaching a squad of players daily, like I did at Spurs, Crystal Palace and Barcelona, it seemed very strange to suddenly have no coaching for weeks on end.

Then, happily, I would get the England lads together - but only for a few days. In that short period, I had to try and get them to change their club style to one I felt essential for the national team. It is not easy to instil a whole new thought processes into someone who has been operating very differently, week in, week out, for his club.

Many of the changes I wanted to make are only minor, I admit. But some are subtle enough to require a great deal of practise and this takes time. But, because of club commitments, time is something an England coach does not have.

On a national level, it is easy to justify clubs releasing England squad players for special training sessions. But it is the clubs that pay the players wages and they want them at every opportunity. As a former club manager, it is a point I understand well. As England coach it does again raise the old arguement of club or country. However, it is a point unlikely to be resolved in the near future.

So, basically, an England coach has to make the best of what time he has with his players. But they are all enthusiastic, mad keen to play for their country and all strive to do well in training. It is not the best situation in the world,but it is the best we are going to get in the foreseeable future.

What a difference it would make if I could have them for, say, a month at a time!

But all our thoughts are now concentrated on the European Cup, which comes at the end of a very gruelling season for our players. I will ensure that we have prepared as thoroughly as possible for a tournament that I see as the toughest next to the World Cup.

Every one of the 15 competing sides will be difficult to overcome. As I said earlier, there are no easy games now. Everyone in the England camp is determined to make a success of it, however, and we are quietly confident. If I said anything more I would be accused of bragging!

I am sure the crowds will come to support us. Their determination for us to do well does transmit itself to the players and is often a vital factor. Finally, I hope and pray they behave themselves and we do not see any repeats of the nastiness and stupidity we witnessed in Dublin.

## ANGLING

June 29
National Championships (Individual).
Contact: National Federation of Anglers
01283 734735.

Aug. 10
National Women's Championships.
Contact: As above.

## ARCHERY

Feb. 14
4th European Indoor Championships. Mol, Belgium. Contact: Grand National Archery Society 01203 696631.

June*
15th Target Championships of Europe and Meditteranean. Kranjska-Gora, Slovenia.

June 10 - 15
15th World Field Championships. Kranska-Gora, Slovenia.

## ATHLETICS

Feb. 1 - 4
European Biathlon Championships. Contact: British Athletic Federation 0121 440 5000.

Mar. 23
24th IAAF/Snickers World Cross Country Championships. Cape Town, South Africa. Contact: Amateur Athletic Association of England 0121 440 5000.

Apr. 21
London Marathon. World class event - entrants run 26 miles from Blackheath to The Mall through the heart of London. Contact: A Ritchie 0171 620 4117.

Apr.14*
National Sports Halls Athletics Finals.
NEC Arena, Birmingham.
Contact: NEC Marketing 0121 780 4141.

Oct. 5
IAAF World Half Marathon Championships.
Palma de Mallorca, Spain.

Dec. 14
European Cross Country Chmpionships.
Charleroi, Belgium.

## BADMINTON

Mar. 29 - 31
English National Championships.
Contact: Badminston Association
of England 01908 568822.

Apr. 14 - 21
European Championships.
Heming, Denmark.

## BALLOONING

Sept.*
10th European Hot Air Balloons
Championships.  Schielleiten, Austria.
Contact: British Balloon and Airship Club
01604 870025.

## BASKETBALL

April*
Budweiser Basketball Championships.
Wembley Arena.
Contact: Basketball League 0121 308 3505.

## BOBSLEIGH

Jan. 29 - Feb. 2
British Championships.
St. Moritz, Switzerland.  Contact:  British
Bobsleigh Association 01985 850064.

Feb. 10 - 25
World Championships.  Calgary, Canada.

## BOWLS

**Mar. 1 - 8**
Indoor Bowls National Championships
(Women). Bannister Park. Contact: English
Women's Indoor Bowling Association 01604
494163.

**Mar. 18**
British Isles Championships (Indoor Bowls).
Llanelli, Wales. Contact: English Indoor
Bowling Association 0181 470 1237.

**Aug. 3**
Women's World Bowls Championships.
Leamington Spa. Contact: English Women's
Bowling Association 01926 430686.

## BOXING

**Mar. 6**
Amateur Boxing National Finals. National
Indoor Arena, NEC, Birmingham. Contact:
Amateur Boxing Association 0181 778 0251.

## CRICKET

**Jan. 2**
5th Test Match - South Africa v England.
Cape Town, South Africa. Contact: TCCB,
Lord's 0171 286 4405.

**Jan. 9**
1st One Day International - South Africa v
England. Cape Town: 2nd at Bloemfontein

(Jan. 11): 3rd at Johannesburg (Jan. 13): 4th at
Verwoersburg (Jan 14): 5th at Durban (Jan.
17): 6th at East London (Jan. 19): and 7th at
Port Elizabeth (Jan. 21).

**Feb. 14 - March 17.**
Cricket World Cup. Various locations India,
Pakistan and Sri Lanka.
**In India**
14 England v New Zealand (Ahmedabad)

16 W. Indies v Zimbabwe (Hyderabad)
17 Holland v NZ (Baroda)
18 India v Kenya (Cuttack)
21 India v W. Indies (Gwallor)
23 Australia v Kenya (Visakhapatnam)
25 Kenya v Zimbabwe (Patna)
27 Australia v India (Bombay)
29 Kenya v W. Indies (Puna)
March
 1 Australia v Zimbabwe (Nagpur)
 2 India v Sri Lanka (Delhi)
 4 Australia v W Indies (Kanpur)
 6 India v Zimbabwe (Kanpur)
 9 Second quarter final (Bangalore)
11 Fourth q/f (Madras)
13 First semi final (Calcutta)
13 Second s/f (Chandigarh)
**In Pakistan**
15 S Africa v United Arab Emirates
(Rawalpindi)
18 England v UAE (Peshawar)
20 NZ v S Africa (Faisalbad)
22 England v Holland (Peshawar)
24 Pakistan v NZ (Lahore)
25 England v S Africa (Rawalpindi)
25 Pakistan v Holland (Lahore)
27 NZ v UAE (Faisalbad)
29 Pakistan v S Africa (Karachi)
March
1 Holland v UAE (Lahore)
3 Pakistan v England (Karachi)
5 Holland v S Africa (Rawalpindi)
6 Pakistan v UAE (Gujranwala)

9 First quarter-final (Faisalbad)
11 Third q/f (Karachi)
17 World Cup Final (Lahore)
**In Sri Lanka**
17 Sri Lanka v Australia (Colombo)

21 Sri Lanka v Zimbabwe (Kandy)
25 Sri Lanka v W Indies (Colombo)
March
6 Sri Lanka v Kenya (Colombo)

June 6 - 10
1st Cornhill Test, England v India.
Edgbaston, Birmingham:
2nd at Lord's (June 20 - 24):
3rd at Trent Bridge, Nottingham (July 4 - 9).

June*
Eton v Harrow annual match at Lord's.

July*
Oxford v Cambridge at Lord's

July 13
Benson & Hedges Cup Final. Lord's.

Aug. 20 - *
Lombard World Challenge Cricket for
Under-15s. Cricket stars of tomorrow
compete in knockout tournament destined
to become annual fixture at Lord's,
Trent Bridge and other leading grounds.

Aug. 29
1st Texaco Trophy Limited-Over
International. England v Pakistan.
Old Trafford, Manchester:
2nd at Edgbaston, Birmingham (Aug. 31): and
3rd at Trent Bridge, Nottingham on (Sept. 1).

Sept. 7
NatWest Bank Trophy Final. Lord's.

April*
Tour of the North of Ireland. Contact:
Northern Ireland Cycling Federation 01247
853705.

June 29 - July 21
Tour de France.

Aug. 28 - Sept. 1
World Championships. Manchester. Contact:
British Cycling Federation 0161 223 2244.

Feb. 10 - 11
Shooting (Air Rifle). Aldersley Stadium,
Wolverhampton. Also Shooting (Air Pistol)
on Feb. 17 - 18. Contact: British Sports
Association for the Disabled 0171 490 4919.

Mar.*
Short Mat Bowls. NIA Community Centre,
Birmingham.

May 11 - 12
Bowls. Alexandra Bowls Centre,
Scarborough.

May 18
Mini Games. Ludwig Guttman Sports Centre,
Aylesbury, Bucks.

June 1 - 2
Swimming. (Long Course) Ponds Forge,
Sheffield.

June 15 - 23
European Tennis Championships.
Eastbourne.

June 29 - 30
Athletics. (Seniors) Alexander Stadium,
Birmingham.

Oct.*
Snooker. John Spencer Snooker Club,
Stirling.

Nov. 2 - 3
Swimming. (Short Course)
Dolphin Centre, Darlington.

## GOLF

May*
Benson and Hedges International.

May - June*
Volvo PGA Championship, Wentworth.

July*
Women's Open.
Contact: Women's Professional Golfers
European Tour 01625 611444.

July 18 - 21
125th British Open. Southport. Contact:
Professional Golfers Association 01675
470333.

July*
Irish Open. Portmarnock, near Dublin.
Contact: Murray Consultants
00 353 1 661 4666.

## GYMNASTICS

May 9 - 12
22nd European Championships (Men).
Copenhagen, Denmark.

May 16 - 19
21st European Championships (Women).
Birmingham. Contact: British Amateur
Gymnastics Association 01952 820330.

May 29 - June 2
12th European Championships.
Oslo/Asker, Norway.

## HANDBALL

May 23 - June 2
2nd European Championships.
Venue to be confirmed.
Contact: British Handball Association
01706 229354.

## HANG GLIDING

Aug. 7 - 18
European Hang Gliding Championships.
Venue to be confirmed.
Contact: British Hang Gliding and
Paragliding Association 0116 261 1322.

## HORSE RACING

Mar. 12 -14
Cheltenham National Hunt Festival.
Cheltenham Gold Cup. Top National hunt
meeting and a particular favourite with the
visiting Irish who attempt to make their
fortunes and drink the place dry. Contact:
Cheltenham Racecourse 01242 513014.

Mar. 28 -30
GRAND NATIONAL.
Steeplechase Meeting. Aintree, Liverpool.
Three-day event culminating in the Grand
National on Saturday, March 30, watched by
television viewers worldwide and a favourite
with housewives who enjoy a "flutter".
Contact: Aintree 0151 523 2600.

73

Apr. 27

Whitbread Gold Cup.
Sandown Racecourse, Esher, Surrey.
Another top event in Britain's
horse racing calendar.
Contact: Racecourse 01372 463072.

May 4
2000 Guineas, Newmarket.
(1000 Guineas on May 5).

June 8
THE DERBY. Epsom Racecourse.
Preceded by The Coronation Cup and
The Oaks. Records of The Derby date back
to 1780 making it one of the world's
oldest recorded sporting events.
Contact: United Racecourses 01372 470047.

June 18 - 21
ROYAL ASCOT.
Ascot Racecourse, Berkshire.
LADIES' DAY - Gold Cup Day -
attended by Queen and other members
of the Royal Family.
THE event of the social calendar
with everyone showing off the latest
fashions, especially hats!
Contact: Grandstand Office 01344 22211.

July 30 - Aug. 3
Glorious Goodwood.
Goodwood Racecourse,
Chichester, West Sussex.
An essential part of the social calendar
and the racing diary.
Contact: Festival Office 01243 774107.

Nov. 15 - 17
National Hunt. The Mackeson at
Cheltenham and The Hennessey at Newbury.
Countryside Raceday at Cheltenham is
normally held the day before the Mackeson.
Contact: Cheltenham Racecourse,
Prestbury Park, Gloucestershire 01242 513014
or Newbury Racecourse 01635 40015.

# Wimbledon's dilemma: New space age stadium - but no new U.K.stars.

**By Buster Mottram (Britain's former number one tennis star).**

Wimbledon 1996 will probably be remembered less for being the 50th post-war event as the last one before its futuristic presentation of top class tennis.

Following the close of play this year, the present Number One court will be demolished and a new 11,000-seater stadium, carved out of the rising ground west of the Centre Court, will be brought into use.

It will be the first stage of the All-England Club's far-seeing development to take their magnesium flare fortnight into the 21st Century.

The plan is brilliant but elegant - championship tennis in a parklike setting - and as ambitious as was the move to the present Church Road site in 1922 when, despite all the White Elephant prophesies, the Centre Court was built.

But, there will not be too many backward glances by the ever increasing number of youthful spectators. Tradition and sentimentality are not for them.

They shout for their favourites and enliven the changeovers with a Mexican wave of two. It is hot dogs and hamburgers at half-time and their strip is tee shirt and trainers. Good luck to the tie-strangled, lounge-suited stuffies sipping their drinks in the Members' pad opposite. A classless, more youthfully oriented and vibrant sporting carnival is evolving.

Much of the geniality which put Wimbledon in the same social bracket as Ascot and Henley has gone. The concourse alongside the Club's main entrance used to be an informal cat-walk for the Ladies' Day fashions. Now it is a one-way system for young fans waiting to catch the arrival of such reigning royals as Pete Sampras, Steffi Graf and Andre Agassi.

The difficult task of accommodating traditional values and modern demands has not been made easier by changes within the game. There have always been cannonball servers at Wimbledon, for example, but now so many men fire unreturnable first balls into court that there are hardly any rallies.

Last June, Wimbledon tried a slightly softer ball to put a break on the serve, but it made hardly any difference. Will they soften it even more for 1996? It is a tricky problem. Rule changes have to be sanctioned internationally.

While Wimbledon is trying to slow things down on grass, countries like France are trying to speed them up by using harder balls on their slow clay courts. It is the surface, not the service that causes the problem.

One of Wimbledon's biggest coming attractions will be the expected return of Monica Seles. The question mark against this dynamic baseliner's ability to recapture the form that made her the world's Number One in 1993 will not be answered until she passes the acid test of Grand Slam competition.

One or two up-and-coming prospects are capable - at least on grass - and only too ready to test Croatian-born Seles, now a United States citizen.

Nineteen-years-old serve-volleying American Lisa Raymond looked particularly promising when she stretched Argentina's Gabriella Sabatini close to breaking point in their quarter final last July.

Another could be Chanda Rubin, the 19-years-old daughter of a U.S. lawyer. She has made impressive progress. The much younger Martina Hingis from Switzerland is clearly another to watch.

Without similarly promising teenagers in this country, British crowds will have to content themselves with cheering on the established order, spearheaded now by ex-Canadian Greg Rusedski, who has recently opted to play for Great Britain.

To get into Wimbledon on merit, players need a computer ranking of around 120 or better. Rusedski is in the 50's. Jeremy Bates, now close to the end of a long career, Mark Petchey and Chris Wilkinson, are less securely placed on the fringe.

Others like Tim Henman, Ross Matheson, Danny Sapsford and Miles Maclagen seem likely to again depend on "wild cards." They will almost certainly be needed for Britain's women players, none presently rated above the 200 level.

The Lawn Tennis Association must be uneasy, to say the least, that so many of our leading players need to use this backdoor entry into Wimbledon.

It is an anachronism that while the All England Club can develop the world's premier championship and stay ahead of the field, Britain seems incapable of producing more than one or two players who can claim to be good enough to take part.

**Dec. 26**
King George VI Chase. Kempton Park.
Walk off the turkey and brandy at the
popular meeting. Contact: Kempton Park
Racecourse 01932 782292.

## ICE SKATING

**Mar. 18 - 24**
World Figure Skating Championships.
Edmonton, Canada.
Contact: National Ice Skating
Association of UK 0171 253 3824.

**March***
Ice Hockey Championships.
Wembley Arena. Four finalists in play-offs
for national championship.
Contact: British Ice Hockey Association
01212 303946.

## JUDO

**Apr. 13**
British Open Championships.
National Indoor Arena, Birmingham.
Contact: British Judo Association
0116 255 9669.

**May 9**
European Senior Championships.
La Haye, Netherlands.

**Oct. 19 - 20**
European Team Championships.
Venue to be confirmed.

## KARATE

**April***
National Karate Championships.
NEC Arena, Birmingham.
Contact: English Karate Governing Body
01225 834008.

## LAWN TENNIS

**May 14 - 18**
British Clay Court Championships (Women).
West Hants Lawn Tennis Club, Bournemouth.

**May 22 - 25**
World Doubles Cup (Women).
Craig Lockhart Tennis Centre, Edinburgh.

**June 10 - 16**
Stella Artois Grass Court Tennis
Championships. Queen's Club, London.
The International Tennis Circuit comes to
town. World stars play in the warm-up for
Wimbledon. Contact: Lawn Tennis
Association 0171 385 4233.

**June 10 - 16**
DFS Classic (Women).
Edgbaston Priory Club,
Birmingham.

**June 17 - 22**
Direct Line Insurance Championships.
Eastbourne. Contact: Lawn Tennis
Association 0171 381 7000.

**June 17 - 22**
Nottingham Open. City of Nottingham
Tennis Centre, Nottingham.

June 24 - July 7
WIMBLEDON LAWN TENNIS
CHAMPIONSHIPS.
All England Club, Wimbledon, SW19.
Top players from all over the world in
THE most prestigious tennis event.
LADIES' FINAL - July 6.
MENS FINAL - July 7.
Contact: All England Club 0181 946 2244.

## MOTOR SPORT

Jan. 20 - 27
Monte Carlo Rally.

*

RAC Rally.
Venue/date to be fixed.
Contact: RAC Motor Sports 01753 681736.

April 14 - 15
Le Mans 24 Hours Race.

July 13*
British Grand Prix.
Damon Hill, Michael Schumacher
and all the Formula One stars arrive at
Silverstone for Britain's premier
motor racing international.
Contact: Silverstone, Towcester,
Northamptonshire 01327 857271.

## MOTORCYCLING

May 27 - June 17
Isle of Man TT Racing.  Toughest races
on the greatest course in the world.
Contact: 01624 686801.

## NETBALL

Feb. 24
England v Scotland International.
Venue to be confirmed.

Contact: All England Netball Association
01462 442344.

Mar. 23
England v Northern Ireland.
Venue to be confirmed.

## OLYMPIC GAMES

July 19
Opening Ceremony, Olympic Stadium,
Atlanta, Georgia, USA.

Aug. 25
Closing Ceremonies.

## ROWING

April 6
UNIVERSITY BOAT RACE.
The Oxford versus Cambridge Boat Race
attracts large crowds to the Thames between
Putney Bridge and Mortlake.
Boat Race Ball at The Savoy in the evening.
Contact: Scope Communications
0171 379 3234.

July 3 - 7
Henley Royal Regatta & World Cup.
Henley on Thames.
Contact: Amateur Rowing ssociation,
0181 748 3632.

Aug. 24 - 31
World Championships.  Aigubelette, France.

## RUGBY LEAGUE

Apr. 27
Silk Cut Challenge Cup Final.
Wembley Stadium.  Contact: The Rugby
Football League 0113 262 4637.

## RUGBY UNION

**Jan. 20**
France v England. Paris.
Contact (for all England matches):
The Rugby Football Union 0181 892 8161.

**Feb. 3**
England v Wales. Twickenham.

**Feb. 17**
Wales v Scotland. Cardiff.

**Feb. 17**
France v Ireland. Paris.

**Feb. 18**
Scotland v Western Samoa. Edinburgh.
Contact: Scottish Rugby Football Union,
0131 337 2346.

**Mar. 2**
Scotland v England. Edinburgh.

**Mar. 2**
Ireland v Wales. Dublin.

**Mar. 16**
Wales v France. Cardiff.

**Mar. 16**
England v Ireland. Twickenham.

**Apr. 20**
CIS County Championship Final.
Twickenham.

**May 4**
Pilkington Cup Final. Twickenham.

**May 11**
Save & Prosper Middlesex Sevens.
Twickenham.

## RUGBY UNION (Women)

**Feb. 3**
England v Wales. Leicester.

**Feb. 17**
France v England. Paris.

**Mar. 2**
Scotland v England. Edinburgh.

**Mar. 16**
Ireland v England. Dublin.

**Apr. 21**
Vladivar Cup Final. Harlequins, London.

## SKI-ING

**Jan. 22 - 28**
FIS World Championships. Leinz, Austria.
Contact: British Ski Federation 01506 884343.

**Feb. 11 - 25**
World Alpine Ski Championships.
Sierra Nevada, Spain.

## SNOOKER

Feb. 4 - 11
Benson & Hedges Masters. Wembley.
Contact: World Professional Billiards and
Snooker Association 0117 974 4491.

Apr. 20 - May 6
Embassy World Championships. Sheffield.

## SOCCER

Mar. 24
Coca-Cola Cup Final. Wembley. Contact:
The Football Association 0171 262 4542.

Mar. 30 - 31
FA Cup semi finals.

May 11
115th FA Cup Final. Wembley.

June 8 - 30
EUROPEAN CUP '96
England are the hosts as Europe's top soccer
nations join combat for arguably the second
most important football event to the World
Cup with the Final at Wembley on June 30.
Can Terry Venables' England repeat their
triumph of 1966 when, again as host nation,
they were triumphant in the World Cup?
Contact: FA  0171 262 4542.

## SPEEDWAY

Aug. 31
British Grand Prix. London.

## SQUASH

April*
Hi-Tec British Open Squash Championships.
Wembley Conference Centre. Contact:
Squash Rackets Association 0181 746 1616.

## SWIMMING

June 22 - July 2
6th Masters World Championships.
Sheffield. Contact: Amateur Swimming
Association 01509 230431.

## TABLE TENNIS

Apr. 25 - May 5
European Championships. Bratislava,
Slovakia. Contact: English Table Tennis
Association 01424 722525.

## TRAMPOLINING

July 6 - 7
National Championships (England).
Kettering, Northants.  Contact: British
Trampoline Federation 0181 863 7278.

Aug. 23 - 25
FIT 19th World Championships.
Slaghaven, Netherlands.

## TUG-of-WAR

Sept. 18 - 21
World Outdoor Championships.
Slaghaven, Netherlands. Contact: Tug-of-War
Association 01494 783057.

## WATERSKIING

Aug. 21 - 25
European Championships.
Vallenbaek, Denmark.
Contact: British Water Ski Federation
0171 833 2855.

## WEIGHTLIFTING

Apr. 8 - 17
European Championships.
Stavangar, Norway.
Contact: British Amateur
Weight Lifters Association 01865 778319.

## WINDSURFING

March*
IMCO World Championships.
France.  Date & venue to be confirmed.
Contact: RYA Windsurfing 01703 629962.

May*
IMCO European Championships.
France.  Date & venue to be confirmed.

# Tougher England prepare for non-stop cricket.

**By Mike Denness
(Former England Test Captain)**

Imagine starting the year in South Africa, finishing it in Sri Lanka or, possibly, Zimbabwe and taking in a whistle-stop tour of India and Pakistan and two summertime treks around England along the way.

It sounds like an interary designed by a travel agent with a strange sense of direction and an even stranger sense of humour.

In fact it is the England cricket team's programme for 1996 which will reveal how much progress they have made towards regaining their position among the world's top Test-playing countries.

The New Year will find them in Cape Town, preparing for the fifth and final Test on their first tour of South Africa for 31 years.

Then it will be straight into a series of seven one-day internationals - in Cape Town, Bloemfontein, Johannesburg, Pretoria, Durban,East London and Port Elizabeth - which will give both sides an opportunity to prepare for the World Cup.

This is being staged in India, Pakistan and Sri Lanka between February 14 and March 17 and there will be little more than three weeks between the end of England's South African tour and their opening World Cup match against New Zealand in the Indian city of Ahmedabad.

England have never won the World Cup, even though they have had home advantage in the first three tournaments which were all staged in this country, with the finals being played at Lord's.

They have reached the final three times - losing to the West Indies at Lord's in 1979, to Australia at Calcutta in 1988 and to Pakistan in Melbourne in 1992 - and they will fancy their chances again this time.

England are particularly well versed in the one-day game - as they should be for the simple reason that they play it more than any other country - and they have plenty of all-rounders who are invaluable in limited-overs cricket.

Bowlers who can bat are particularly important and England have players like Darren Gough and Dominic Cork, who have made such an impact over the last 12 months, as well as more seasoned performers like Phillip DeFreitas and Mike Watkinson.

Not that it will be easy. The World Cup will make enormous demands on the teams as nine Test-playing countries plus Holland, Kenya and United Arab Emirates criss-cross the sub-Continent before the tournament reaches its climax in Lahore.

There will be little respite for the England players before the start of the home season and two demanding back-to-back Test series against India and Pakistan.

They may not have quite the same appeal as Australia and the West Indies but they could hardly be more challenging. India have a wealth of talented batsmen, led by the little genius Sachin Tendulkar, a combative all-rounder in Manoj Prabhakar, and two outstanding bowlers in Javagal Srinath and Anil Kumble, who made a huge impression with Gloucestershire and Northamptionshire respectively last summer.

As for Pakistan, they have had their problems in recent times both at home and abroad, but they will always be a force in world cricket as long as they have Wasim Akram and Waqar Younnis to spearhead their attack.

England's cricket year is scheduled to end with a tour of Sri Lanka, who beat them the last time they were there, and, perhaps, a brief trip to Zimbabwe, though these have yet to be confirmed.

It may sound glamourous, but it is hard work being an international cricketer these days - and spare a thought for the umpires as well.

They are under even greater pressure than the players in this age of television replays and the best of them spend just as much of their lives travelling the world since the formation of the National Grid International Panel.

It was set up in 1993 when the International Cricket Council, the game's ruling body, invited each of the nine Test-playing countries to nominate two umpires with "the experience, the ability and availability" to stand in Test matches.

England were asked to nominate an additional two because they have more full-time professional umpires than any other country and now one member of the 20-strong panel stands as a "visiting" umpire alongside an umpire appointed by the home country in every Test match.

## EVENTS & CARNIVALS

**United Nations 50th Anniversary.**
In January 1946 the first General Assembly
of the UN met at Central Hall, Westminster.
The Hall will house celebrations of the historic
anniversary.  Commemorative Concert (10);
Lecture (13) and Church Service (14).
Contact: Central Hall 0171 222 8010.
(Jan.10 - 14)

**Holiday On Ice.**
Spectacular family variety show, Wembley Arena.
Contact: 0181 900 1234.
(Jan. 30 - 18 Feb.)

**January Sales.**
Wear Out Your Credit Card, it's January Sales
time. Shop Till You Drop at Harrods, Barkers,
Peter Jones - everyone has bargains!  Oxford
Street, Knightsbridge, local High Streets.
See Evening Standard for details. (Jan. 1 - 31)

**Chinese New Year Celebrations.**
Soho, London W1.  Dragon dances, traditional
Chinese music and entertainment welcome the
start the Year of the Rat.  Contact: Mr. Malcolm
Man or Mr. K. Wu  0171 734 5161. (Feb. 25)

**The Great British Innovation & Inventions Fair.**
British inventiveness is legendary.
Will this NEC, Birmingham, show
inspire a new generation?
Contact: Fair Organiser 01202 762252.  (Feb.*)

**Tenth BT Swimathon.**
Tens of thousands take part in sponsored
swimming events all over the country.
Contact: 0171 406 7335.
(Feb. 29 - March 3)

**LEAP YEAR events.**
Newspaper columns full of ladies using
their traditional right to ask a partner's
hand in marriage!  (Feb 29)

**Roaring Twenties Festival.**
Killarney, Co. Kerry, Eire.
Contact: Ms Alex Baradi 00 353 64 41170.
(March 15 - 18)

**LONDON MARATHON.**
Twenty five thousand runners - from
internationals to fun-runners - pound
26 miles of central London streets in this
internationally recognised event, one of
the best organised marathons in the world.
Millions are raised for charities.
Contact: 0171 620 4117. (Apr. 21)

**Blackheath Kite Festival.**
Colourful day as dozens show off
their kite-flying skills.
Contact: Lewisham Council press office
0181 695 6000 x 6079.
(Date to be fixed)

**Devon County Show at Exeter.**
Contact: Festival Office 01392 713875.
(May 16 - 18)

**The 95.8 Capital FM Extravaganza.**
Zany, crazy, nutty - fun. Capital's live events
show featuring activities galore. Details and
venue to be confirmed.
Contact: Trades Exhibitions 0171 610 3001.
(May 24 - 28)

**Richmond May Fair.**
Richmond Green, Richmond-on-Thames.
Contact: 0181 948 4464. (May 11).

**Richmond Festival.**
Open-air riverside events
of music, street performers and special
Richmond Theatre programme.
Contact: Arts Festival Office 0181 332 0534.
(July 6 - 21).

**Greenwich Festival.**
From the Maritime Museum to the Cutty Sark,
all are involved in the Festival.
Contact: 0181 317 8687. (May 24 - June 9)

**Three Counties Show.**
Malvern, Worcestershire.
Agriculture, horticulture, equestrian and County
Set social event.  Contact: Showground
01684 892751. (June11 - 13)

**City of London Festival.**
St. Paul's Cathedral and the Tower of London
are among the fabulous historic City buildings
housing the annual arts festival.
Contact: City Arts Trust 0171 377 0540.
(June 26 - July 14)

**London to Brighton Bike Ride.**
Motorists become second-class citizens as
27,000 cyclists - from speed-kings to veterans
on sit-up-and-beg bikes - pedal 52 miles to
raise funds for the British Heart Foundation.
Last year's event raised a million pounds.
Contact:  British Heart Foundation
0171 935 0185. (June 16)

**London Strollathon.**
Last year more than 20,000 strolled the London
streets in aid of charity.  Contact: Elizabeth
Dawes 0171 353 6060.  (July 14*)

**Earth Galleries.**
Natural History Museum, South Kensington.
Opening of spectacular  three-storey galleries
that cost £12-million on the site of the former
Geological Museum featuring latest in teaching
and information techniques.
Contact: Natural History Museum 0171 938 9388.
(July*)

**Royal National Eisteddfod.**
Llandeilo, Dyfed.  Welsh-speaking cultural
festival.  Contact:  Welsh Tourist Office
01222 499909.  (Aug. 3 - 10)

**International Balloon Fiesta.**
Awesome sight as up to 150 balloons or
inflatables lift into the sky from Ashton Court
Estate, Bristol.  Contact: Bristol Tourist
Information 0117 926 0767.  (Aug. 9 - 11)

**Balloon and Vintage Car Fiesta.**
Leeds Castle, Maidstone Kent.  Up to 25
colourful hot air balloons take to the skies
above Leeds Castle. Contac:t 01622 765400.
(June 1 - 2*)

**International Women's Day Show.**
Hackney Empire, Mare Street, London E8.
Contact: Box Office 0181 985 2424. (Mar. 8)

**World Pipe Band Championships.**
Pipe band championships and Highland Games.
Contact: Scottish Pipe Band Association
0141 221 5414.  (Aug. 17)

## NOTTING HILL CARNIVAL.
Europe's biggest street carnival.
Live stages. Children's Carnival Day is Sunday.
Band spectacular is on Monday.
Contact: Festival Office 0181 964 0544.
(Aug. 25 - 26)

## Bexley Festival.
Two weeks of special events including
music, theatre and the annual Bexley Show
at Danson Park, Bexleyheath.
Contact: Ms Bax 0181 303 7777. (July 6 - 21)

## Rose of Tralee Festival.
Co. Kerry, Eire.
Contact: Festival Office 00 353 66 21322.
(Aug. 24 - 31)

## The Edinburgh International Festival.
World's largest celebration of arts attracting inter-
national figures to numerous events. Contact:
Festival Office 0131 226 4001.
(Aug. 11 - 31)

## Edinburgh Fringe Festival.
Now larger than the main event.
Music, dance, children's events.
More than 400 performances daily.
Contact: Festival Fringe Society 0131 226 5257.
(Aug. 11 - 31)

## Edinburgh International Film Festival.
Documentaries, lectures and events.
Contact: Filmhouse 0131 228 4051.
(Aug. 10 - 25)

## Royal Highland Gathering.
Braemar, Scotland. Popular with Royals
staying at nearby Balmoral. The kilted Clansmen,
bagpipes, Highland Dancing, Caber-tossing.
Contact: Gathering Office 01339 755377.
(Sept. 7)

## European Women of Achievement Luncheon.
Grosvenor House Hotel, W1.
Contact: Tricia Birchley 01923 283770.
(Autumn date to be announced)

## International Eisteddfod.
Llangollen, North Wales. This colourful
event attracts the world to the annual
international gathering featuring music,
dance, poetry and Welsh culture.
Contact: Welsh Tourist Office 01222 499909.
(Sept. 9 - 14)

## Chinatown Mid Autumn Festival.
Lion dancing, Chinese Theatre, singing and
variety on stage at Gerard Street, Chinatown.
Contact: Malcolm Man or K. Wu 0171 734 5161.
(Sept. 10)

## DAILY MAIL INTERNATIONAL SKI SHOW.
Olympia. The UK's top ski event.
Contact: ANGEX 01895 677677.
(Oct. 26 - Nov. 3)

## Natural History Museum.
British Gas Wildlife Photographer of the Year.
Contact: Natural History Museum 0171 938 9388.
(Oct. *)

**Grand Firework Spectacular.**
Floodlit Leeds Castle is wonderful backdrop to breathtaking display of fireworks.
Contact: Leeds Castle, Maidstone, Kent 01622 765400. (Nov. 2)

**London Film Festival.**
National Film Theatre, South Bank, SE1 and other venues.
Contact: Press Office 0171 928 3535.
(Nov. *)

**Fantasy In The Sky Fireworks Spectacular.**
Flambards Village Theme Park, Helston, Cornwall.
Contact: David Edwards 01326 573404.
(Oct. 26)

**25th Grand Firework Display.**
Crystal Palace Park.
Contact: Ian Middleton 0181 699 1363.
(Nov. 5)

## EXHIBITIONS (HOBBIES & ACTIVITIES)

**International Model Engineer and Modelling Exhibition.**
Grand Hall, Olympia, Hammersmith, London W14. Hundreds of radio controlled boats, cars etc. Contact: Mrs. Christine Basden, Exhibition Manager 01442 66551. (Jan. 1 - 5)

**Knitting, Needlecraft and Design Exhibition.**
Sandown Park Exhibition Centre, Esher, Surrey.
From cross-stitch to patchwork quilting.
Contact: Robert Ewin,
Nationwide Exhibitions UK Ltd. 0117 970 1370.
(Jan. 18 - 21)

**VHF Convention.**
The Radio Society of Great Britain meets.
Sandown Park Convention Centre, Esher Surrey.
Contact: Peter Kirby 01707 659015. (Feb 18)

**International Practical Woodworking Exhibition.**
Wembley Exhibition Hall. Europe's largest show for woodworking enthusiasts.
Contact: Tony Kynaston, Sovereign Exhibition Management 0181 773 3751.
(Feb 22 - 25)

**British Philatelic Exhibition, Spring Stampex.**
Royal Horticultural Halls, Greycoat Street, London SW1. Collectors from all over the world enter displays. Contact: Miss Lindsay Towle, Stampex Ltd., British Philatelic Centre 0171 490 1005. (Feb. 27-Mar. 3)

**Record and CD Collectors' Fair.**
Jolson, Beethoven, Presley or Satchmo - all there at the NEC, Birmingham. Contact: Exhibitions Manager, NEC 0121 780 4141 or P & J Promotions 01273 463017.
(Mar. 16 - 17)

**Sewing for Pleasure.**
Major attraction for veteran stitchers and school children alike at the NEC, Birmingham.
Contact: International Craft & Hobby Fair Ltd. 01425 272711. (Mar. 14 - 17)

**Miniatura.**
NEC, Birmingham. Major exhibition for collectors and lovers of the world in miniature.
Contact: Miniatura 0121 783 2070. (Mar. 16 -17)

**London International Dive Show.**
Everything for the sub-aqua enthusiast or professional. Equipment, retailers, diving boats and holidays or training courses.
Contact: The Dive Show Ltd. 0181 977 9878.
(Mar. 23 - 24)

**Careers 2000.**
Careers, Training, Education and Jobs event. NEC, Birmingham.
Contact: Jarvis Exhibitions 0181 464 4129.
(Mar. 10 - 11)

**Alexandra Palace Antiques & Collectors' Fair.**
Contact: Pig and Whistle Promotions 0181 883 7061. (Mar. 10)

### Bike '96. Olympia.
Test track to try out the new "wheels". Massive collection of bikes and accessories, help and advice plus cycling club, competition and holidays.
Contact: Future Events 01225 442244.
(Mar. 29 - 31)

### Toy and Train Collectors' Fair.
NEC, Birmingham. The Antiques Roadshow and other TV programmes have seen a booming interest in toys ancient and modern.
Contact: D & J Fairs 01526 398198. (Mar. 31)

### The Alexandra Palace Spring Craft Fair.
Contact: Marathon Event Management 0181 665 1082. (Apr. 6 - 8)

### York Model Railway Show.
York Racecourse.
See grown men become enthusiastic schoolboys amid massive displays of model railway layouts.
Contact: Michael Cook 01653 694319.
(Apr. I6 - 9)

### Spring Needlecraft Fair. Olympia.
Displays from museums and needlecraft school feature along with everything to do with needlecraft.
Contact: Chris Dawn,
Future Events 01225 442244.
(Apr. 11 - 14)

### The Sugarcraft Show.
Culinary inventiveness and sculpting skills at Sandown Park Convention Centre, Esher.
Contact: Gerry Fox,
Aspen Litharne 01789 720604. (Apr. 12 - 14)

### Consumer Electronics Show.
Earls Court, SW5.
Gadgets and widgets galore with the latest in electronic products.
Contact: Blenheim Exhibitions 0181 742 2828.
(Sept.)

### National Franchise Exhibition.
Olympia.
For those interested in taking the plunge to become their own boss or change their career.
Contact: Blenheim Exhibitions Group plc 0181 742 2828. (Apr. 12 - 14)

### The National Woodworker Show.
Something for everyone who loves working with wood. Sandown Park Conference Centre, Esher, Surrey.
Contact: John Lenton,
Nexus Special Interests 01442 66551.
(Sept. 26 - 29)

### Chelsea Craft Fair.
Chelsea Old Town Hall, Kings Road.
Contact: Craft Council 0171 278 7700.
(Sept. 15 - 27)

### The Alexandra Palace Antique & Collectors' Fair.
London N22. Contact: Pig & Whistle Promotions 0181 883 7061. (Sept.*)

### International Jewellery Exhibition.
Earls Court. Showpiece event featuring latest merchandise to tools and machinery.
Contact: Earls Court 0171 370 8011.
(Sept. 1 - 4*)

### Knitting & Stitching Show.
Alexandra Palace N22.
Contact: Gordon Thomas 0181 690 8888.
(Oct*)

**Royal Miniature Society's
101st annual exhibition.**
Central Hall, Westminster.  Fascinating
miniatures from paintings to sculpture.
Contact: Sue Barton 017496 74472.
(Nov. 8 - 23)

**The Dolls House Fair.**
Alexandra Palace, London N22.
Fabulous collection of houses and minute
fittings, furniture and even cutlery.
Contact: AP Exhibition Office 0181 365 2121.
(Nov - 9*)

**British Philatelic Exhibition, Autumn Stampex.**
Royal Horticultural Halls, Greycoat Street,
London SW1. Second major show with collectors
from all over the world entering displays.
Contact: Miss Lindsay Towle, Stampex Ltd.,
British Philatelic Centre 0171 490 1005.
(Oct. 22 - 27)

**The Teddy Bear Fair.**
Alexandra Palace, London N22.
Teddy lovers travel from afar for this popular fair.
Contact: AP Exhibition Office 0181 365 2121.
(Nov. 8 - 9*)

**Job Scene London.**
Alexandra Palace, London N22.
Contact: AP Exhibition Office 0181 365 2121.
(Nov.*)

**Healing Arts.**
Royal Horticultural Society Halls, SW1.
Contact: Mrs. Spar 0171 938 3788.  (Nov.)

**Good Woodworking Show.**
Alexandra Palace, N22.  Contact: Future
Publishing 01225 442244.  (Nov *)

## FASHION & BEAUTY

**You and Your Wedding Live.**
Everything for the bride to be:
top designers, fashion shows and
exhibitions at Central Hall, Westminster.
Contact: You & Your Wedding
Magazine 0171 437 0791.  (Jan. 20)

**London Bridal Fair.**
Alexandra Palace, N22. And who said marriage
was outmoded and weddings a thing of the past?
Contact: National Bridal Fairs 01423 530588.
(Jan. 27 - 28)

**Midland Bridal Fair.**
After January's London fairs for brides-to-be
or the wannabes, Midlands lasses have their
turn at the large NEC, Birmingham, fair.
Contact: National Bridal Fairs,
Harrogate. 01423 530588.  (Feb. 17 - 19)

**Goldilocks Fashion Show.**
The Savoy, Strand, London WC2.
Famous names and faces among fabulous
top-name fashions.  In in aid of the NSPCC.
Contact: Jane Woodfield 0171 336 7738.
(Mar. 15)

**London Fashion Week.**
Thirty shows to challenge the world of high
fashion and streetwear.  Colleges, designers,
students and fashion houses present their latest
styles. (Oct. - Nov.*).
*See Evening Standard for details.*

**Afro Hair & Beauty Exhibition.**
Alexandra Palace, London N22.
Contact: Afro Hair & Beauty Ltd. 0181 883 7061.
(May 26 - 27)

**NSPCC BERKELEY DRESS SHOW.**
Berkeley Hotel, SW1.
Top social event in addition to
fashion occasion.  In aid of the NSPCC.
Contact: Joanna Hurthouse 0171 336 7738.

**The Natural Health Show.**
National Hall, Olympia.
Natural health and therapy, beauty,
health food, exercise and aerobics.
Contact: Global Events 0181 347 6661.
(July 11 - 14)

**Alternative Fashion Week.**
Old Spitalfields Market, London E1.
Contact: Alternative Arts 0171 375 0441.
(Mar. 18 - 22)

## FLORAL & HORTICULTURAL

**CHELSEA FLOWER SHOW.**
The UK's No. 1 Flower Show. The Queen
arrives in horse-drawn carriage on first day.
Royal Hospital grounds, SW3. (Monday, Tuesday
and Wednesday are RHS Members' days).
Open to public Thursday and Friday.
Contact: 0171 396 4696   (May 21 - 24).
*Flower Show Gala Charity Preview.*
*Contact: Mandy Hills,*
*RHS Special Events 0171 630 5999.*

**Royal Ulster Agricultural Society Spring Show.**
Northern Ireland's premier agricultural and
horticultural show at Balmoral, Belfast.
Contact: RUAS 01232 665225. (Feb. 21)

**RHS Orchid Show.**
RHS Old Hall, Westminster.
Contact: Lisa Aitkan 0171 636 7422.  (Mar. 9 - 10)

**Spring Gardens Week.**
Leeds Castle, Maidstone, Kent.
Contact: 01622 765400.  (Mar. 23 - 31)

**Harrogate Spring Flower Festival.**
Valley Gardens, Harrogate, North Yorkshire.
Britain's largest Spring Show.
Contact: Lisa Aitkan 0171 636 7422 or North of
England Horticultural Society 01423 561049.
(Apr. 26 - 28)

**Malvern Spring Garden Show.**
Three Counties Showground,
Malvern, Worcestershire.
Contact: Showground 01684 892752.
(May 10 - 12)

**County Wicklow Gardens Festival.**
Eire. Contact: Brendan O'Connor 00 353 404
66058.  (May 17 - 23)

**BBC Gardeners' World Live.**
NEC, Birmingham.  Contact: BBC Haymarket
Exhibitions 0171 402 2555.  (June 12 - 18*)

**Wisley RHS Flower Show.**
Wisley RHS Garden, Surrey.
Contact Lisa Aitkan 0171 636 7422.
(June 28 - 29)

**GREAT YORKSHIRE SHOW.**
Harrogate, Yorkshire.  Top annual
agricultural and horticultural show
featuring livestock and machinery.
Contact: Yorkshire Agricultural
Society 01423 561536.
(July 9 - 11)

**Spalding Flower Parade and Festival.**
Millions of blooms adorn floats for the annual
parade followed by static displays.
Contact: Springfields 01775 724843.
(May 4 - 6)

**RHS Hampton Court Palace International Flower Show.**
East Molesey. Largest event of its kind in the world. Contact: Sylvia Holder, RHS 0171 267 6022.
(July 9 - 14)
*Charity Gala Evening.*
*Contact: RHS Special Events 0171 630 5999.*

**International Spring Fair.**
NEC, Birmingham.
Contact: National Exhibition Centre 0121 780 4141. (Feb. 4 - 8)

**City of London Flower Show.**
Guildhall, EC2.
Contact: Mr. Jones 0181 472 3584.
(Sept. 10 - 11)

**Great Autumn Flower Show.**
Harrogate, Yorkshire. National flower organisations and top nurserymen provide displays at this premier event.
Contact: North of England Horticultural Society 01423 561049.
(Sept 13 -15)

**Royal Horticultural Society Great Autumn Show.**
London RHS Halls, Westminster.
Contact: RHS 0171 267 6022.
(Sept. 17 - 18)

**Jersey Battle of Flowers.**
Described as one of the top three floral festivals in Europe. Sectacular floats, music, dancing and singing.
The famous Moonlight Parade is on the 9th.
Contact: Jersey Battle of Flowers Association 01534 30178. (Aug. 8-9)

**The Spitalfields Show.**
Annual Horticultural Show in the Old Spitalfields Market, London E1.
Contact: Alternative Arts 0171 375 0441.
(Sept. 15)

## FOOD & DRINK

**The BBC Good Food Show 1996.**
Olympia. Top chefs, samples galore, wine tasting
at one of Britain's major cooking and kitchen
events. You may need to diet afterwards!
Contact: Consumer Exhibitions Ltd.
0181 948 1666. (Mar. 7 - 10)

**Sussex Beer Festival.**
Hove Town Hall, West Sussex.
Dozens of real ales, traditional ciders and perries.
Contact: Festival Organiser 01903 261225.
(Feb. 23 - 25)

**The Great British Beer Festival.**
Olympia, W14.
CAMRA, the campaign for real ale, presents
more than 500 British and foreign beers and
ciders in what it describes as "the glory of
British cask-conditioned beer".
Contact: Campaign For Real Ale Ltd.
01727 867201. (Aug. 6 - 10)

**Food and Drink Expo '96.**
NEC, Birmingham.
Contact: Blenheim Events 0181 742 2828.
(Apr. 28 - May 1)

**Festival of English Wines.**
Leeds Castle, Maidstone, Kent.
Jazz backing to tasting of the fruit of
southern English vineyards.
Contact: Leeds Castle 01622 765400.
(May 14-15*)

**Festival of Food & Farming.**
Hyde Park, London. Contact: 01484 428326.
(May 9 - 12)

**Cyprus Wine Festival.**
Alexandra Palace, London N22.
Contact: Parikiaki 0171 272 6777. (June 29 - 30)

**Galway Oyster Festival.**
Contact: Ms Ann Flanagan 00 353 91 22066.
(Sept. 26 - 29)

**London Docklands Seafood Fair.**
Isle of Dogs. Contact: 0171 512 4414. (Aug.*)

**International Festival of Fine Wine and Food.**
Olympia 2, W14.
Contact: Gary Thompson 0171 782 6874. (Oct.*)

**The World's Biggest Coffee Morning.**
The British Heart Foundation hopes to beat its
own Guinness world record by encouraging
people all over the country to go for coffee
between 8-12 at pre-arranged locales.
Last time 500,000 took part. An awful lot of
coffee. Proceeds to the British Heart Foundation.
Contact: BHF 0171 935 0185. (Oct.)

**20th International Kinsale Gourmet Festival.**
Co Cork, Eire.
Contact: Peter Barry 00 353 21 774026. (Oct. 6)

**Fast Food Fair.**
Metropole Exhibition Centre, Brighton.
Leading trade event covering equipment
to franchises.
Contact: Reed Exhibition Companies
0181 910 7910. (Apr. 6 - 11)*

## HOMES

**DAILY MAIL IDEAL HOME EXHIBITION.**
Earls Court Exhibition Centre.
The biggest consumer home show in the UK -
now a national institution - featuring every
conceivable product and service for the home.
More than 650 exhibitors.
Contact: Earls Court 0171 373 8141
or DMG Angex Ltd. 01895 677677.
(Mar. 14 - Apr.7)

**The Individual Homes,**
**Home Building & Renovating Show.**
An inspiration for the DIY fanatic, home restorer
or build-it-yourself devotee. NEC, Birmingham.
Contact: Centaur Exhibitions 0171 287 5000.
(Mar. 7 - 10)

**National & Overseas Homebuyer Show.**
Olympia.  Largest property sale of
UK and overseas homes.
Contact: Homebuyer Events Ltd. 0181 877 3636.
(Mar. 8 - 10)

**The National Self-Build Homes Show.**
Alexandra Palace, London N22.
Contact: AP Exhibition Office 0181 365 2121.
(Sept.).

**Autumn Ideal Home Exhibition.**
After the splendour of the Earls Court venue,
home-makers or improvers have another chance
to see the latest in consumer products at the
NEC, Birmingham. Contact: NEC 0121 200 2222.
(Oct. 18 - 27)

**Daily Telegraph**
**Period Homes and Gardens Show.**
Olympia.
Style and home improvements for
period homes and gardens.
Contact:  01733 394304.  (Feb. 6 - 11)

## JAZZ

**Spring Into Jazz.**
Barbican Centre, EC2.  Two day festival
featuring top names and programmes.
Contact: Barbican Centre 0171 638 8891.
(May 8 - 9)

**Glasgow International Jazz Festival.**
Euro-reputation and presence at top jazz event.
Contact: Ms Jill Rodger 0141 552 3552.
(June 28 - July 7)

**Edinburgh International Jazz Festival.**
Marching bands, late night events,
dances and hundreds of musicians
at various Edinburgh venues.
Contact: Festival Office 0131 557 1642.
(Aug. 3 - 10)

**Brecon Jazz Festival.**
Organisers pack 80 jazz concerts
into the unique three-day festival.
Contact: Festival Office 01874 635557.
(Aug. 9 - 11)

**Soho Jazz Festival.**
The sounds of New Orleans take
over in pubs, theatres and even churches
as Soho stomps to jazz.
Contact: Robert Guterman 0171 437 6437.
(Sept 26 - Nov 5)

**Jazz Night at Claremont.**
National Trust landscaped gardens at Claremont,
Esher, Surrey, are the perfect backdrop for a night
of summer Trad and Blues.
Contact:  Eloise Harris 01372 453401.
(July 14)

**Cork Jazz Festival.**
The southern Irish city hosts
Eire's major jazz event of the year.
Contact: Ms Emily Twomey 00 353 21 270463.
(Oct. 25 - 28)

**Kew Gardens Jazz.**
The magnificent setting of the Royal Botanic
Gardens and its Conservatory would be better
suited to orchestral masterpieces.  But the small
matter of the Gardens being on the main flight-
path into Heathrow Airport precludes that.  So
jet-deafening jazz is the answer.  Contact:  Kew
Gardens 0181 332 5616.  (July 16 - 20).

**Jazz Bands at Cambridge Big Day Out.**
Up to 13,000 take to the ancient city
centre for a jazz parade and fireworks.
Contact:  Cambridge Tourism 01223 358977.
(July 13)

**Jazz Plus.**
Victoria Embankment Gardens, London WC2.
Open-air season of contemporary
jazz and multi-cultural music.
Contact: Alternative Arts 0171375 0441.
(June* - July*)

## LEISURE, CARAVAN & CAMPING

### Scottish Boat, Caravan, Camping and Leisure Show.
Scottish Exhibition and
Conference Centre, Glasgow.
They travel from the Highlands and the
Lowlands for the large range of equipment
and displays at Scotland's own show.
Contact: Associated Eventex. Tel: 0141 204 0123.
(Feb. 7 -11)

### National Boat, Caravan and Leisure Show.
NEC, Birmingham.
A must for Outdoor Types with wide
selection of boats, mobile homes,
camping and touring equipment.
Contact: BPM Exhibitions 0121 236 3366.
(Feb. 17 - 25)

### International Canoe Exhibition.
NEC, Birmingham.
Holiday and adventure exhibition featuring
lectures and pool displays in addition to wide
range of canoes and accessories.
Contact: Peter Ingram,
British Canoe Union 01903 795500.
(Feb. 24 - 25)

## MOTOR SPORT & TRANSPORT

### 100th RAC London to Brighton Veteran Car Run.
Probably the oldest continuous motoring
event in the world immortalised by the film
Genevieve. From Hyde Park to Brighton.
Contact: Colin Wilson 01753 681736. (Nov. 3)

### Autosport International.
NEC, Birmingham.
High-octane show for lovers of all forms of
motor sport. Contact: Haymarket Exhibitions
0171 402 2555. (Jan. 4 - 7)

### International Performance Motor Show.
Boy racers, racy ladies and enthusiasts'
opportunity to enjoy the best in motorsport
developments or witness Judge Dredd's
fabmobile. Olympia, London W14.
Contact: 3D events 0181 744 1585.
(Jan 15 - 18)

### British Grand Prix.
Damon Hill, Michael Schumacher and all the
Formula One stars arrive at Silverstone for
Britain's premier motor racing international.
Contact: Silverstone, Towcester,
Northamptonshire 01327 857271. (July 13)

### Road Racing & Superbike Show.
Alexandra Palace, N22. It's become a cult show drawing not only power-mad youngsters but grandads who used to have a BSA Bantam. Plenty of safety equipment and advice, too. Contact: Shire PR & Marketing 01703 629962. (Feb. 1 - 4)

### The London Classic Motor Show.
Alexandra Palace, N22.
Contact: Greenwood Exhibitions 01296 631181. (Mar. 16 - 17)

### BBC Top Gear Classic and Sportscar Show.
NEC, Birmingham. Contact: BBC Haymarket Exhibitions 0171 402 2555. (May 4 - 6)

### Isle of Man TT Racing.
Toughest races on the greatest course in the world. Contact: 01624 686801. (May 27 - June 17)

### Le Mans 24-hour Race.
The classic endurance event attracting drivers and visitors from all over the world. An absolute must if you suffer from insomnia.

### Balloon and Vintage Car Fiesta.
Leeds Castle, Maidstone, Kent. Strictly for those who prefer a slower pace. Vintage cars parade as up to 25 colourful hot air balloons take to the skies. Contact: 01622 765400. (June1 - 2)

### Louis Vuitton Concourse d'Elegance Classic Car Competition.
Hurlingham Club.
Top social event. Invitation Only. (June 1)

### Festival of Speed, Goodwood.
Against the backdrop of Goodwood House, near Chichester, the Festival - Top Vehicles by Invitation Only - has become the world's biggest event of its kind attracting international attention. Contact: Festival Office 01243 774107. (June 21 - 23)

### The London to Brighton Classic Car Run for pre-1979 vehicles. *(NOT the Veteran Car Run).*
Starting Norman Park, Bromley.
Contact: Sally Greenwood 01296 631181
(June 9)

### Mid-Wales Festival of Transport.
Rally of road and agricultural transport and equipment - some dating from early 1800s - in parades and displays at Powis Castle, Welshpool.
Contact: Mike Exton 01938 553680.
(July 13 -14)

### Highclere Castle Classic Car Show.
Newbury, Berks. Capability Brown's gardens are the setting for Classic Cars from all over Europe. Contact: Greenwood Exhibitions 01296 631181. (July 23)

### Knebworth '96 Classic Car Show.
Knebworth Park, Stevenage, Herts. Up to 1,000 classic cars attract 12,000 visitors annually. Two hundred autojumble and trade stands. Contact: Greenwood Exhibitions 01296 631181. (Aug. 25 - 26)

**Sixth annual Classic Car and Country Show.**
Losely Park, Guildford. Summer-special
in aid of the Queen Elizabeth Foundation
for Disabled People.
Contact: Mrs. Elizabeth Jordan 01372 842204.
(Aug. 3 - 4)

**Bromley Pageant of Motoring.**
Norman Park, Bromley. Contact: John Wexham
0181 658 3531. (June 30)

**British International Motor Show.**
NEC, Birmingham. Thousands will dream
or drool over the motor industry's latest models.
Press on Oct. 15, Trade 16-18.
Contact: NEC Marketing 0121 780 4141.
(Oct. 19 - 26)

## MUSIC & OPERA

**BBC HENRY WOOD
PROMENADE CONCERTS.**
Royal Albert Hall, Kensington Gore, SW7.
As much a part of Summer and England
as strawberries and cream.
LAST NIGHT OF THE PROMS
(Sept. 14) by Ticket-only.
Contact: Nicola Gould 0171 765 4296.
(July 19 - Sept. 14)

**GLYNDEBOURNE FESTIVAL
OPERA SEASON.**
Internationally-known festival presents
a season of top opera productions.
Contact: Festival Office 01273 812321.
(May 15 - Aug. 24)

**Bath International Festival.**
Avon. Concerts, jazz, opera, exhibitions and
talks at various venues around the Spa town.
Contact: Festival Office: 01225 462231.
(May 17 - June 2)

**KNELLER HALL OPEN AIR
CONCERT SEASON.**
Royal Military School of Music concerts,
Kneller Hall, Twickenham, Middlesex.
Fanfares, jazz, dance, military and light music are
among the selections for 1996 open air concerts.
Contact: Capt. Ian Peaple 0181 898 8629.
(May - July)

**Hampton Court Palace Music Festival.**
The magnificent royal palace by the Thames.
Warm summer evenings and music to match.
Contact: Donna Gelardi 0181 781 9507.
(June 6 - 20)

**49th Aldeburgh Festival of Music and Arts.**
Founded by Benjamin Britten, Aldeburgh includes
opera, concerts, exhibitions and literary events.
Contact: Aldeburgh Foundation 01728 452935.
(June 7 - 23)

**Kensington Symphony Orchestra:**
**Korngold: Die Tote Stadt.**
Royal Festival Hall (Hayward Gallery).
Contact: RFH  0171 921 0800. (Jan. 14)

**BBC Symphony Orchestra.**
Under Andrew Davis, celebrating work of
American composer Charles Ives at the Barbican
Centre. Contact: 0171 638 5403.  (Jan. 19 - 21)

**Belfast Music Festival.**
Balmoral, Belfast.
More than 2,000 young people compete
in this prestigious music, drama and speech
competition. Held annually since 1911 it has
earned international fame.
Contact: Nancy Mackinnon 01232 611537.
(Mar. 4 - 16)

**Mobil Concert Season.**
Leading musicians and orchestras at
Royal Naval College Chapel, Greenwich.
Contact: 0181 305 1818 or 0181 317 8687  (Mar.
14 & Apr. 25)

**William Walton Festival.**
Queen Elizabeth Hall, Oldham,
Greater Manchester.
The composer's family are refurbishing a
Victorian conservatory in celebration of the
Festival of Oldham-born Sir William.
Contact: Festival Office 0161 911 4072.
(Mar. 15 - 17)

**Leeds International Concert Season.**
International performers in an
internationally-recognised event.
At the Town Hall, Leeds, Yorkshire.
Contact: Miss Esther Harrison 0113 247 8336.
(Sept. 3 - 21)

**Claremont Fete Chempetre.**
Claremont Gardens, Esher, Surrey.
In aid of National Trust.
Contact: Eloise Harris 01372 453401.
(July 10 - 13)

**Reception & Gala Concert.**
Light opera and classics plus Dinner at
The Guildhall, City of London.
In aid of  the National Deaf Children's Society.
Contact: John Trotter 0171 585 1606.  (Mar. 20)

**Chelsea Opera Group.**
Beethoven: Leonora or Bellini: Norma.
Queen Elizabeth Hall, Royal Festival Hall,
London SE1.
Contact: 0171 921 0800.  (Mar. 24)

**West Sussex International**
**Youth Music Festival.**
Music and dance groups from all
over the world perform at various venues.
Contact: Concertworld UK 0171 401 9941.
 (Apr. 4 - 9)

**Harrogate International Youth Music Festival.**
Choirs, bands, orchestras and dance
groups from many parts of the world perform
at various North Yorkshire venues.
Contact: Concertworld UK 0171 401 9941.
(Apr. 5 - 12)

**Leeds International Music Festival.**
Recitals and concerts of contemporary
music, jazz and Indian music.
Contact: Artistic Director,
Dr. Graham Hearn 0113 245 2069.
(May 4 - 12)

**BOC Covent Garden Festival.**
Covent Garden, giving young opera artists
chance to perform to wider audiences.
Contact: 0171 240 0930.  (May 6 or 13)

**Beverley Early Music Festival.**
Medieval architecture and fine music
in unique event at various locations in
Beverley, Humberside.
Contact: 01904 658338.  (May 9 - 12)

**Bournemouth International Festival.**
Up to 80 venues are needed to house
events ranging from opera, rock and
jazz to dance and poetry.
Contact: Mrs. T. Weeks 01202 297327.
(May 11 - 26)

### Newbury Spring Festival.
Berks.
Music - from orchestral performances to jazz - feature in this festival of music and the visual arts.
Contact: Sheilagh Jackson 01635 32421.
(May 14 - 18)

### Isle of Wight International Oboe Competition.
Contact: Administrator 01983 612451. (June*)

### National Music Day.
Mick Jagger's idea of a national day to encourage musical talent and enjoyment enters 4th year in 1996. People all over country can take part by organising an event and registering it with National Music Day Events.
Contact: 0171 629 8912. (June1 - 30)

### Spitalfields Festival.
Early music and solo recitals in the 18th Century Wren-pupil church of Christ Church Spitalfields.
Contact: Kate Cockburn 0171 377 0287.
(June 5 - 26)

### Leeds Castle Open Air Concerts.
Leeds Castle, Maidstone, Kent.
Carl Davis conducts the Royal Liverpool Philharmonic Orchestra. Climax is the 1812 Overture with guns of the Royal Artillery and fireworks spectacular.
Contact: Leeds Castle 01622 765400.
(June 29 & July 6)

### Shrewsbury Int. Music Festival.
Languages from around the world fill the Shropshire county town as music and dance groups perform at various venues.
Contact: Concertworld UK 0171 401 9941.
(June 28 - July 5)

### Chelsea Opera Group.
Puccini: Gianni Schicchi - Il Tabarrao: Suor Angelica. South Bank (Queen Elizabeth Hall).
Contact: 0171 763 0800. (June 9)

### Syon Park Opera.
The Great Conservatory at Syon House, Brentford, Middlesex, houses summer opera in aid of The Foundation for Children with Leukaemia.
Contact: Suzanne Macrae 0171 404 0808.
(June 24 - 28)

### York Early Music Festival.
The perfect setting for recitals of ancient music.
Contact: Festival Office 01904 658338.
(July 5 - 14)

### Llangollen International Music Eisteddfod.
The annual event's reputation now attracts musicians from more than thirty countries.
The Choir of the World competition is among the major attractions.
Contact: Eisteddfod Office 01978 860236.
(July 9 - 14)

### Welsh Proms '96.
St. David's Hall, The Hayes, Cardiff.
Leading British orchestras perform in the annual series of promenade concerts.
Contact: St. David's Hall 01222 342611.
(July 11 - 20)

### Buxton Opera Festival.
Spectacular settings in the Spa Town adjoining the Peak District National Park.
Operatic recitals, cabaret, children's events.
Contact: Festival Office 01298 70395.
(July 18 - Aug. 4)

### Stowe Music and Fireworks.
Stowe Landscape Garden, Buckinghamshire.
In aid of the National Trust.
Contact: Katie Williams 01494 528051. (July)

### Snape Proms.
Snape Maltings, home of the Benjamin Britten-inspired and more highbrow Aldeburgh Festival, lets its hair down in this one-month excitement of rock, jazz, folk, dance and orchestral mayhem.
Snape Maltings, Aldeburgh, Suffolk.
Contact: Proms Office 01728 453543.
(Aug. 1 - 31)

**North Wales Music Festival.**
St. Asaph, Clwyd. Choirs, soloists and music
in the splendour of rugged North Wales.
Contact: Welsh Tourist Office 01222 499909.
(Sept. 16 - 22)

**Wexford Opera Festival.** Eire.
Contact: Jerome Hynes 00 353 53 221447. (Oct.)

**Huddersfield Contemporary Music Festival.**
Held at various locations around West Yorkshire,
the internationally-recognised festival will
feature, in addition to contemporary music,
theatre, film and dance.
Contact: Festival Office 01484 425082.
(Nov. 20 - Dec. 1)

**Belfast Festival at Queen's.**
From folk and opera to classical.
Queen's University, Belfast, houses music
as well as drama and cinema in its
annual celebration of the arts.
Contact: Festival Director,
Michael Barnes 01232 667687. (Nov. 9 - 27)

**City of London Sinfonia at the Barbican.**
Charity concert in aid of Help the Aged.
Contact: 0171 253 2926. (Dec.)

**London Music Show.**
Wembley Exhibition and Conference Centre.
Contact: Kathryn Abbatt 01353 665577. (Dec.)

**Henley Festival of Music and the Arts.**
Jools Holland and James Galway are expected
to play at concerts in the Thames-side town - in
festival mood after the Henley Regatta - as it
stages musical events for all tastes at many
venues. Includes open-air riverside music.
Contact: Festival Office 01491 411353.

**Open Air Opera Season.**
Victoria Embankment Gardens, WC2.
Contact: Alternative Arts 0171 375 0441.
(June - July*)

**British Gas Wildlife Photographer of the Year.**
From 17,000 entries taken by photographers all
over the world, the last 100 in the competition
for the coveted title are displayed at the
Natural History Museum, Cromwell Road,
South Kensington.
Contact: Gina Dobson 0171 938 9123.
(Jan. 6 - Feb 29)

**Edwardian Women Photographers exhibition.**
Bodelwyddan Castle, nr Rhyl, North Wales
(Jan. 14 - Mar. 19). National Portrait Gallery
touring exhibition. Other venues: Derby Museum
and Art Gallery (April 8 to May 21) and Batley Art
Gallery, West Yorkshire.
Contact: 0171 306 0055 (Sept. 2 - 30)

**Photographs by Beaton
and his contemporaries.**
Exhibition. Photograph Gallery,
National Portrait Gallery, St. Martin's Place, WC2.
Contact: 0171 306 0055. (June 28 - Sept. 22)

## POP, FOLK & ROCK

**Glastonbury Festival
of Contemporary Performing Arts.**
You don't have to have had hippy parents
to go - but it helps. Glastonbury took
over where Woodstock left off.
Contact: Glastonbury Festivals 01749 890470.
(June 28 - 30*)

**Phoenix Festival.**
Stratford-Upon-Avon. Rock, jazz, acoustic,
dance and alternative healing.
Contact: Mean Fiddler Organisation
0181 961 5490. (July 11 - 14)

### Beatles Festival.

Liverpool. Merseysiders celebrate
The Fab Four with music and entertainment
at their old stomping ground.
Contact: The Cavern Club 0151 236 9091.
(Aug 23 - 27)

### Reading Festival.

Largest Alternative Music Festival in the world.
Music on two stages, comedy on third.
Contact: Mean Fiddler Organisation
0181 961 5490. (Aug. 23 - 25*)

### British Music Fair.

Find a friend with a trade ticket to get you
into this strictly 'General Public not admitted'
event featuring the latest in keyboards, pianos,
printed music, audio and software.
Contact: British Music Fairs 0181 907 8314.
(July 21 - 23)

### The Fleadh.

Van Morrison and Bob Dylan popped in at
previous events. Major open-air Irish music
festival at Finsbury Park, London N4.
Contact: The Mean Fiddler Organisation
0181 961 5490. (June 8 - 15)

### Cambridge Folk Festival.

Cherry Hinton Hall grounds. International line-up
for annual festival which includes presentations of
ethnic folk in addition to popular tastes.
Contact: Mr. E. Barcan 01223 358977.
(July 26 - 28)

### Festival of Dover.

Pop, classic and jazz - with maritime
theme for '96 - beneath the White Cliffs.
Contact: Miss S. Pascoe 01304 821199.
(May 27-June 7)

## PARLIAMENTARY

### STATE OPENING OF PARLIAMENT.

The Queen rides in State with mounted escort
from the Household Cavalry from Buckingham
Palace to the Houses of Parliament to formally
open the Parliamentary session and read the
traditional Queen's Speech announcing the
proposals of HM Government.
(Probably Nov. '96)

### Palace of Westminster All Party Ladies' Committee Children's Easter Party.

Contact: Mrs. William Gunnery 0181 746 8311.
(March 29)

### House of Lords v House of Commons Tug o' War event.

Abingdon Green, Westminster. In aid of
Cancer Relief Macmillan Fund. Other teams
include secretaries, clergymen and soldiers.
Dinner in College Gardens follows.
Contact: Jane Cowmeadow 0171 887 8249.
(July)

**House of Lord v Commons
Speedo Charity Swim.**
Hurlingham Club. In aid of Women's Caring Trust.
MPs take on Members of the House of Lords in
this annual challenge match which is nearly
always won by The Lords.
Contact: 0171 730 8883.  (Nov 25*)

## RIVER THAMES

### UNIVERSITY BOAT RACE.
The Oxford versus Cambridge Boat Race began
140 years ago and has attracted crowds to the
four miles of the Thames between Putney Bridge
and Mortlake ever since.  Charity Boat Race Ball
at The Savoy in the evening.
Contact: Scope Communications 0171 379 3234.
(Apr. 6)

### Henley Royal Regatta.
Five-day international rowing event - but
becoming better-known as a social and fashion
MUST.  Watch the strict dress code, ladies.
Contact: 01491 572153.  (July 3 - 7)

**Devizes to Westminster
International Canoe Race.**
Up to 300 canoes set off from Devizes
for the 150-mile trip along the Kennet & Avon
Canal to the Thames at Reading and thence
to Westminster Bridge. Thousands line the
route to cheer the entrants on.
Contact: Competition Secretary 0171 401 8266.
(Apr. 5 - 8)

**Barge Driving Race.**
Annual Lightermen's race - and day out for
Thames folk - as teams of one Freeman and two
Apprentices steer cargo barges on the incoming
tide from Greenwich.
Contact: Bob Crouch, The Waterman's Company
0171 283 2373.  (Date to be set)

**Doggett's Coat and Badge Race.**
In the early 1700s, Irish comedian
Thomas Doggett could not find a Waterman,
the taxi-drivers of the day, to take him from the
Old Swan, London Bridge, to his lodgings in
Chelsea.  So he donated an orange coat and
silver badge to the winner of a wherry race.
Started in 1715, the race claims to be the oldest
annually-recorded sporting event in the world.
Contact: Bob Crouch, The Waterman's Company
0171 283 2373.  (July*)

**London Thames Festival.**
From Teddington to Barking.
Week of events on or by the River Thames
include art, music and sporting activities.
Contact: London Thames Festival office
0171 700 6453. (Sept.*)

**The Great River Race.**
Viking Boats, Chinese
dragonboats, Hawaiian war canoes compete in
race from Richmond to Isle of Dogs. Includes
entries from the US, Sweden, Holland and
France.
Contact: Stuart Wolff
0181 398 9057.
(Sept.*)

**Shrimpers' Regatta.**
Age-old sailing and rowing races in
traditional craft at Gravesend, Kent.
Contact: Bob Crouch, Waterman's Company
0171 283 2373. (Dates to be set)

## SHIPS, YACHTS & BOATS

**LONDON INTERNATIONAL BOAT SHOW.**
Earls Court Exhibition Centre, London SW5.
Family-fun at world's favourite boat show,
now in its 42nd year featuring over 800 craft.
Contact: British Marine Industries Federation
01784 473377. (Jan. 5 - 14)

**Southampton International Boat Show.**
Mayflower Park, Southampton - largest of its
kind in Europe. Yachts, chandlery, satellite
technology and all aspects of marine activities
for the ocean sailor and those who just like
messing about on the river.
Contact: British Marine International
Federation 01784 473377.
(Sept. 15 - 23)

### Cowes WEEK.

Isle of Wight. Social set crosses the Solent to link with the Sailing set for the annual Cowes event featuring all classes of yacht racing. Royals often attend and Prince Philip has used the Royal Yacht Britannia as his base in the past. Numerous parties and charity balls (Royal Yacht Squadron Ball, Salamander Ball and Cowes Ball). Contact: Cowes Combined Clubs 01983 295744. (Aug. 3 - 10)

### Singlehanded Transatlantic Yacht Race.

Starts from Queen Anne's Battery, Plymouth, Devon, and finishes in Newport, Rhode Island, USA. Contact: Royal Western Yacht Club 01752 660077. (June 16)

### Sailboat Show.

Alexandra Palace, N22.
Cast off, landlubbers, and set course for THE event of the dinghy fraternity. More than 70 dinghies fill the two halls attracting fair weather sailors to international helmspersons. Organiser: Royal Yachting Association 01703 629962. (Mar. 2 - 3)

### Festival of the Sea.

Bristol.
City's historic dockyard fills with 1,000 craft to celebrate Britain's maritime history. The highpoint will be the launching of replica of John Cabot's ship the "Mathew' at the harbour. Contact: Festival Office 0117 922 1996. (May 24 - 27)

**Bedford River Festival.**
The Great Ouse attracts 200 rivercraft, 80 floats and 1,000 performers in one of the biggest outdoor events of the year.
Contact: Ms Pat Simpson, Bedford Council 01234 221 622. (May 25 - 26)

**Cutty Sark Tall Ships Race.**
Crews will take part in two races in '96 - to The Baltic and The Med.
Contact: Peter Smales, The International Sail Training Association 01590 683900.
(July 6 - 13)

**EUROPEAN POWERBOAT CHAMPIONSHIPS.**
Southport, Lancs.
Thrills and hopefully no spills as entrants from many countries compete in this spectacular event.
Contact: Jim Cunliffe 01704 533791.
(July 6 - 7)

**Dartmouth Royal Regatta.**
Devon.
The West of England Rowing Championships are among boating and sailing events at this popular annual event overlooked by the Royal Naval College, Dartmouth.
Contact: Regatta Office 01803 832435.
(Aug. 29 - 31)

**Lloyds Bank Harbour Regatta.**
Bristol. Popular annual event in the historic harbour at Bristol.
Contact: Brlstol Tourism 0117 929 7704.
(July 28 - 28*)

## TRAVEL

**Holiday World.**
King's Hall, Balmoral, Belfast.
Leading international travel exhibition.
Contact: Holiday & Leisure Fairs, Dublin.
Phone: 00 3531 295 7418. (Jan. 17 - 21)

**Destinations '96.**
National travel show giving expert advice and information on hundreds of holiday locations from Australia to Zimbabwe with celebrity speakers and hundreds of exhibitors.
Contact: Consumer Exhibitions 0181 948 1666.
(Feb. 15 - 18)

**British Travel Trade Fair '96.**
What's the "hot" holiday spot of the year? What's in? Out? Where are the bargains?
The big trade get-together at NEC, Birmingham.
Contact: English Tourist Board 0181 846 9000.
(Mar. 20 - 21)

**World Travel Market.**
Earls Court. The global travel industry forum.
Contact: Earls Court Exhibition Centre 0171 370 8011. (Date to be set)

# THEATRE & ENTERTAINMENT

**SHAKESPEARE THEATRE SEASON.**
Royal Shakespeare Theatre, Swan Theatre and
The Other Place, Stratford-upon-Avon,
Warwickshire.  New productions plus selection
of plays at various venues including major
new travelling season programme to be
announced in the Spring of 1996.
Contact: Royal Shakespeare
Theatre 01789 295623
or Information Line 01789 295623.
(Jan 1 - Dec.)

**REGENTS PARK
OPEN AIR THEATRE SEASON.**
Inner Circle, NW1.
New Shakespeare Company.
On a warm, dry night it is idyllic.
But it's sometimes the Bard with Brolly
or some pretty unusual "sounds off" from
the inmates of nearby London Zoo.
Contact:  Sheila Benjamin 0171 935 5756.
(May 31 - Sept. 7)

**Minack Theatre Summer Season.**
Porthcurno, Penzance, Cornwall.
Dramatic clifftop open-air theatre sets fabulous
backdrop to season of plays and musicals.
Contact: Theatre Management 01736 810181.
(Aug. 20 - Sept. 13)

**Summer Season of Street Theatre.**
Soho Square, W1; Paddington Street Gardens,
W1 and Victoria Embankment Gardens, WC2.
Contact: Alternative Arts 0171 375 0441.
(June* - July*)

**Move-It Mime Festival.**
Victoria Embankment Gardens, WC2.
Contact:  Alternative Arts 0171 375 0441.
(June 8 - 9)

**International Animation Festival.**
St. David's Hall, Cardiff.
The art of cinema animation.
Contact: British Film Institute,
London 0171 255 1444. (May 26 - June 2)

**National Amateur Performing
Arts Competition.**
Marking the 75th anniversary of the
British Federation of Festivals,
major contests (also on July 13 - 14)
to find winners at University of Warwick.
Contact: Competition Hotline 0114 230 3557.
(June 20-21)

**Irish Life Dublin Theatre Festival.**
Contact: Tony O'Dalaigh 00 353 1 677 8122.
(Oct. 7 - 19)

**Polesdon Lacey Open Air Theatre Season.**
Great Bookham, nr Leatherhead, Surrey.
Tempest (June 19 - 22); Anything Goes
(June 26 - 29); Rigoletto (July 4 - 6)
and BBC Big Band (July 7).
Contact: Eloise Harris 01372 453401.

**Shakespeare in Spitalfields.**
Old Spitalfields Market, London E1.
Contact: Alternative Arts 0171 375 0441.
(Oct. 13)

## JANUARY 1996

| | | |
|---|---|---|
| MON | 1 | _____ |
| TUE | 2 | _____ |
| WED | 3 | _____ |
| THUR | 4 | _____ |
| FRI | 5 | _____ |
| SAT | 6 | _____ |
| SUN | 7 | _____ |
| MON | 8 | _____ |
| TUE | 9 | _____ |
| WED | 10 | _____ |
| THUR | 11 | _____ |
| FRI | 12 | _____ |
| SAT | 13 | _____ |
| SUN | 14 | _____ |
| MON | 15 | _____ |
| TUE | 16 | _____ |
| WED | 17 | _____ |
| THUR | 18 | _____ |
| FRI | 19 | _____ |
| SAT | 20 | _____ |
| SUN | 21 | _____ |
| MON | 22 | _____ |
| TUE | 23 | _____ |
| WED | 24 | _____ |
| THUR | 25 | _____ |
| FRI | 26 | _____ |
| SAT | 27 | _____ |
| SUN | 28 | _____ |
| MON | 29 | _____ |
| TUE | 30 | _____ |
| WED | 31 | _____ |

## FEBRUARY 1996

| | | |
|---|---|---|
| THUR | 1 | _____ |
| FRI | 2 | _____ |
| SAT | 3 | _____ |
| SUN | 4 | _____ |
| MON | 5 | _____ |
| TUE | 6 | _____ |
| WED | 7 | _____ |
| THUR | 8 | _____ |
| FRI | 9 | _____ |
| SAT | 10 | _____ |
| SUN | 11 | _____ |
| MON | 12 | _____ |
| TUE | 13 | _____ |
| WED | 14 | _____ |
| THUR | 15 | _____ |
| FRI | 16 | _____ |
| SAT | 17 | _____ |
| SUN | 18 | _____ |
| MON | 19 | _____ |
| TUE | 20 | _____ |
| WED | 21 | _____ |
| THUR | 22 | _____ |
| FRI | 23 | _____ |
| SAT | 24 | _____ |
| SUN | 25 | _____ |
| MON | 26 | _____ |
| TUE | 27 | _____ |
| WED | 28 | _____ |
| THUR | 29 | _____ |

## MARCH 1996

| | | |
|---|---|---|
| FRI | 1 | _____ |
| SAT | 2 | _____ |
| SUN | 3 | _____ |
| MON | 4 | _____ |
| TUE | 5 | _____ |
| WED | 6 | _____ |
| THUR | 7 | _____ |
| FRI | 8 | _____ |
| SAT | 9 | _____ |
| SUN | 10 | _____ |
| MON | 11 | _____ |
| TUE | 12 | _____ |
| WED | 13 | _____ |
| THUR | 14 | _____ |
| FRI | 15 | _____ |
| SAT | 16 | _____ |
| SUN | 17 | _____ |
| MON | 18 | _____ |
| TUE | 19 | _____ |
| WED | 20 | _____ |
| THUR | 21 | _____ |
| FRI | 22 | _____ |
| SAT | 23 | _____ |
| SUN | 24 | _____ |
| MON | 25 | _____ |
| TUE | 26 | _____ |
| WED | 27 | _____ |
| THUR | 28 | _____ |
| FRI | 29 | _____ |
| SAT | 30 | _____ |
| SUN | 31 | _____ |

## APRIL 1996

| | | |
|---|---|---|
| MON | 1 | _____ |
| TUE | 2 | _____ |
| WED | 3 | _____ |
| THUR | 4 | _____ |
| FRI | 5 | _____ |
| SAT | 6 | _____ |
| SUN | 7 | _____ |
| MON | 8 | _____ |
| TUE | 9 | _____ |
| WED | 10 | _____ |
| THUR | 11 | _____ |
| FRI | 12 | _____ |
| SAT | 13 | _____ |
| SUN | 14 | _____ |
| MON | 15 | _____ |
| TUE | 16 | _____ |
| WED | 17 | _____ |
| THUR | 18 | _____ |
| FRI | 19 | _____ |
| SAT | 20 | _____ |
| SUN | 21 | _____ |
| MON | 22 | _____ |
| TUE | 23 | _____ |
| WED | 24 | _____ |
| THUR | 25 | _____ |
| FRI | 26 | _____ |
| SAT | 27 | _____ |
| SUN | 28 | _____ |
| MON | 29 | _____ |
| TUE | 30 | _____ |

## MAY 1996

| | | |
|---|---|---|
| WED | 1 | _____ |
| THUR | 2 | _____ |
| FRI | 3 | _____ |
| SAT | 4 | _____ |
| SUN | 5 | _____ |
| MON | 6 | _____ |
| TUE | 7 | _____ |
| WED | 8 | _____ |
| THUR | 9 | _____ |
| FRI | 10 | _____ |
| SAT | 11 | _____ |
| SUN | 12 | _____ |
| MON | 13 | _____ |
| TUE | 14 | _____ |
| WED | 15 | _____ |
| THUR | 16 | _____ |
| FRI | 17 | _____ |
| SAT | 18 | _____ |
| SUN | 19 | _____ |
| MON | 20 | _____ |
| TUE | 21 | _____ |
| WED | 22 | _____ |
| THUR | 23 | _____ |
| FRI | 24 | _____ |
| SAT | 25 | _____ |
| SUN | 26 | _____ |
| MON | 27 | _____ |
| TUE | 28 | _____ |
| WED | 29 | _____ |
| THUR | 30 | _____ |
| FRI | 31 | _____ |

## JUNE 1996

| | | |
|---|---|---|
| SAT | 1 | _____ |
| SUN | 2 | _____ |
| MON | 3 | _____ |
| TUE | 4 | _____ |
| WED | 5 | _____ |
| THUR | 6 | _____ |
| FRI | 7 | _____ |
| SAT | 8 | _____ |
| SUN | 9 | _____ |
| MON | 10 | _____ |
| TUE | 11 | _____ |
| WED | 12 | _____ |
| THUR | 13 | _____ |
| FRI | 14 | _____ |
| SAT | 15 | _____ |
| SUN | 16 | _____ |
| MON | 17 | _____ |
| TUE | 18 | _____ |
| WED | 19 | _____ |
| THUR | 20 | _____ |
| FRI | 21 | _____ |
| SAT | 22 | _____ |
| SUN | 23 | _____ |
| MON | 24 | _____ |
| TUE | 25 | _____ |
| WED | 26 | _____ |
| THUR | 27 | _____ |
| FRI | 28 | _____ |
| SAT | 29 | _____ |
| SUN | 30 | _____ |

## JULY 1996

| | | |
|---|---|---|
| MON | 1 | _____ |
| TUE | 2 | _____ |
| WED | 3 | _____ |
| THUR | 4 | _____ |
| FRI | 5 | _____ |
| SAT | 6 | _____ |
| SUN | 7 | _____ |
| MON | 8 | _____ |
| TUE | 9 | _____ |
| WED | 10 | _____ |
| THUR | 11 | _____ |
| FRI | 12 | _____ |
| SAT | 13 | _____ |
| SUN | 14 | _____ |
| MON | 15 | _____ |
| TUE | 16 | _____ |
| WED | 17 | _____ |
| THUR | 18 | _____ |
| FRI | 19 | _____ |
| SAT | 20 | _____ |
| SUN | 21 | _____ |
| MON | 22 | _____ |
| TUE | 23 | _____ |
| WED | 24 | _____ |
| THUR | 25 | _____ |
| FRI | 26 | _____ |
| SAT | 27 | _____ |
| SUN | 28 | _____ |
| MON | 29 | _____ |
| TUE | 30 | _____ |
| WED | 31 | _____ |

## AUGUST 1996

| | | |
|---|---|---|
| THUR | 1 | _____ |
| FRI | 2 | _____ |
| SAT | 3 | _____ |
| SUN | 4 | _____ |
| MON | 5 | _____ |
| TUE | 6 | _____ |
| WED | 7 | _____ |
| THUR | 8 | _____ |
| FRI | 9 | _____ |
| SAT | 10 | _____ |
| SUN | 11 | _____ |
| MON | 12 | _____ |
| TUE | 13 | _____ |
| WED | 14 | _____ |
| THUR | 15 | _____ |
| FRI | 16 | _____ |
| SAT | 17 | _____ |
| SUN | 18 | _____ |
| MON | 19 | _____ |
| TUE | 20 | _____ |
| WED | 21 | _____ |
| THUR | 22 | _____ |
| FRI | 23 | _____ |
| SAT | 24 | _____ |
| SUN | 25 | _____ |
| MON | 26 | _____ |
| TUE | 27 | _____ |
| WED | 28 | _____ |
| THUR | 29 | _____ |
| FRI | 30 | _____ |
| SAT | 31 | _____ |

## SEPTEMBER 1996

| | | |
|---|---|---|
| SUN | 1 | _____ |
| MON | 2 | _____ |
| TUE | 3 | _____ |
| WED | 4 | _____ |
| THUR | 5 | _____ |
| FRI | 6 | _____ |
| SAT | 7 | _____ |
| SUN | 8 | _____ |
| MON | 9 | _____ |
| TUE | 10 | _____ |
| WED | 11 | _____ |
| THUR | 12 | _____ |
| FRI | 13 | _____ |
| SAT | 14 | _____ |
| SUN | 15 | _____ |
| MON | 16 | _____ |
| TUE | 17 | _____ |
| WED | 18 | _____ |
| THUR | 19 | _____ |
| FRI | 20 | _____ |
| SAT | 21 | _____ |
| SUN | 22 | _____ |
| MON | 23 | _____ |
| TUE | 24 | _____ |
| WED | 25 | _____ |
| THUR | 26 | _____ |
| FRI | 27 | _____ |
| SAT | 28 | _____ |
| SUN | 29 | _____ |
| MON | 30 | _____ |

## OCTOBER 1996

| | | |
|---|---|---|
| TUE | 1 | _____ |
| WED | 2 | _____ |
| THUR | 3 | _____ |
| FRI | 4 | _____ |
| SAT | 5 | _____ |
| SUN | 6 | _____ |
| MON | 7 | _____ |
| TUE | 8 | _____ |
| WED | 9 | _____ |
| THUR | 10 | _____ |
| FRI | 11 | _____ |
| SAT | 12 | _____ |
| SUN | 13 | _____ |
| MON | 14 | _____ |
| TUE | 15 | _____ |
| WED | 16 | _____ |
| THUR | 17 | _____ |
| FRI | 18 | _____ |
| SAT | 19 | _____ |
| SUN | 20 | _____ |
| MON | 21 | _____ |
| TUE | 22 | _____ |
| WED | 23 | _____ |
| THUR | 24 | _____ |
| FRI | 25 | _____ |
| SAT | 26 | _____ |
| SUN | 27 | _____ |
| MON | 28 | _____ |
| TUE | 29 | _____ |
| WED | 30 | _____ |
| THUR | 31 | _____ |

## NOVEMBER 1996

| | | |
|---|---|---|
| FRI | 1 | _____ |
| SAT | 2 | _____ |
| SUN | 3 | _____ |
| MON | 4 | _____ |
| TUE | 5 | _____ |
| WED | 6 | _____ |
| THUR | 7 | _____ |
| FRI | 8 | _____ |
| SAT | 9 | _____ |
| SUN | 10 | _____ |
| MON | 11 | _____ |
| TUE | 12 | _____ |
| WED | 13 | _____ |
| THUR | 14 | _____ |
| FRI | 15 | _____ |
| SAT | 16 | _____ |
| SUN | 17 | _____ |
| MON | 18 | _____ |
| TUE | 19 | _____ |
| WED | 20 | _____ |
| THUR | 21 | _____ |
| FRI | 22 | _____ |
| SAT | 23 | _____ |
| SUN | 24 | _____ |
| MON | 25 | _____ |
| TUE | 26 | _____ |
| WED | 27 | _____ |
| THUR | 28 | _____ |
| FRI | 29 | _____ |
| SAT | 30 | _____ |

## DECEMBER 1996

| | | |
|---|---|---|
| SUN | 1 | _____ |
| MON | 2 | _____ |
| TUE | 3 | _____ |
| WED | 4 | _____ |
| THUR | 5 | _____ |
| FRI | 6 | _____ |
| SAT | 7 | _____ |
| SUN | 8 | _____ |
| MON | 9 | _____ |
| TUE | 10 | _____ |
| WED | 11 | _____ |
| THUR | 12 | _____ |
| FRI | 13 | _____ |
| SAT | 14 | _____ |
| SUN | 15 | _____ |
| MON | 16 | _____ |
| TUE | 17 | _____ |
| WED | 18 | _____ |
| THUR | 19 | _____ |
| FRI | 20 | _____ |
| SAT | 21 | _____ |
| SUN | 22 | _____ |
| MON | 23 | _____ |
| TUE | 24 | _____ |
| WED | 25 | _____ |
| THUR | 26 | _____ |
| FRI | 27 | _____ |
| SAT | 28 | _____ |
| SUN | 29 | _____ |
| MON | 30 | _____ |
| TUE | 31 | _____ |

# I N D E X

109